AMERICA SINGS

Stories and Songs of Our Country's Growing

Arrangements by

EDWIN JOHN STRINGHAM

Illustrations by

ELIZABETH BLACK CARMER

AMERICA SINGS

Stories and Songs of Our Country's Growing

COLLECTED AND TOLD BY

CARL CARMER

NEW YORK: ALFRED · A · KNOPF

CONTENTS

[*The titles set in* SMALL CAPITALS *are the names of songs*]

EAST

MIDWEST

SOUTH

FAR WEST

PREFACE

A FEW MONTHS AGO I happened to see in a bookstore a shelf of books of French folk-songs published for the pleasure of young people in the United States. As I opened one of the books and saw the colored pictures and the music for *Sur le Pont d'Avignon, Il Pleut Bergère, Au Clair de la Lune* and other songs out of the meadows and forests of France, it occurred to me that American boys and girls had no such book from which to sing songs out of their own woods and fields and streams, the words and tunes of their own country. Students of the nation's music have published collections of these songs, it is true, but only for grown-ups who, like themselves, want to preserve folk-verses and folk-tunes as a part of the country's historical background. The more I thought about this, the more I wished to see a book of our native folk-songs arranged and edited for young Americans to sing.

After I had begun trying to find the songs which American folks have been making up and singing at their work and at their play for three hundred years, the idea on which my mind started work that day in the bookshop began to stretch and grow. When the first white people came to the shores of North America they found that to make homes for themselves and to live well in this vast new country, great jobs had to be done—jobs that took years of solid work before showing results. And since at that time there was no easy way for them to amuse themselves as we do now, with radio or movie or phonograph, our great-grandfathers and great-grandmothers told each other stories and sang each other songs which they made up out of their thoughts about the hard work they were doing. For instance, when the earliest settlers saw that the land was covered with trees, they set to work to cut them down in order that fields might be cleared and cabin-homes built. As they worked, their axes rose and fell in rhythm, and soon the cutters were making up a song to sing to the steady beat. And after the day's work was done and they saw how little of the great woods had been cut, they went home at night to rest and to make up stories after supper, about a hero so big and so strong he could clear whole forests all by himself in a day. Each swing of his axe, they would say, opened up an acre of sunshine in the dark woods.

That is how Paul Bunyan and Tony Beaver came to be the great heroes of the stories made up by the men who swing the axes—the lumberjacks or shanty-men as they call themselves, because they cut the trees into lumber and because, when they are at work in the woods, they live in long wooden shanties. In the same way, after the early Americans who went west had set numberless cattle to grazing on the treeless grassy plains, the brave hard-riding cowboys who herded them and took care of them made up songs to the rhythms of galloping hooves, as their mustangs swung tirelessly along. And at night, after the cook had fed them from the chuckwagon, they sat by their campfires and made up stories about great cowboys like Pecos Bill who could do easily deeds that were known to be impossible for other men.

When this book began to take shape I selected a lumberjack story and told it in my own way, as all tellers of folk-stories do, and I made the story lead right into the singing of a lumberjack song. I made my cowboy story lead right into the singing of a cowboy song. I did the same thing with the stories and songs of coal-miners and gold-miners, of raftsmen and canalers and steamboaters, of whalers and fishermen, of cotton-pickers and farmers, of hunters and pirates, of soldiers and scouts and Texas Rangers. When I got through, it seemed to me that these stories and songs had told the history of America in their own way. I believed that even more strongly when I read that my friend, Stephen Vincent Benét, had said something which was printed in the Book Magazine of the Sunday *New York Times* and which went like this:

"It's always seemed to me that legends and yarns and folk-tales are as much a part of the real history of a country as proclamations and provisos and constitutional amendments. The legends and the yarns get down to the roots of the people—they tell a good deal about what people admire and want, about what sort of people they are. You can explain America in terms of formal history; you can also explain it in terms of Rip Van Winkle and Paul Bunyan, of Casey Jones and Davy Crockett—not the Crockett whose actual exploits are in the history books—but the Crockett who was a legend during his lifetime—the frontiersman up on his hind legs. And once you start digging into the latter sort of material you get more and more fascinated."

Mr. Benet could truthfully have said that folk-songs do the same thing as do the legends. I have tried to put the stories *and* the songs together in such a way that they tell not only the romantic history of our land but also how we worked with our hands at our jobs, and how much we did.

Mr. Edwin John Stringham, whom I persuaded to put down the musical notes for the songs, has, I think, done his job wisely and well. He and I first put our heads together to make the tunes fit the words and the words fit the tunes without giving up any of the meaning and spirit of either one. In most of the scholarly books of folk-songs for adults, it is necessary to take a running start and sing through regardless—letting extra notes and extra syllables fall where they may. In this book Mr. Stringham and I think we have made the words and music go together pretty well. I have tried to select from the songs, many of which are very long and meant mostly for grown-up singing, only those verses which tell something of our country and its people and which would be fun for boys and girls to sing.

Mr. Stringham has tried to arrange the tunes so that they are fun to sing, too, and he has made the songs easy to play on the piano— so that a teacher or a mother or a boy or a girl who can play a little will not find them too hard. He has also stayed away from notes that are either too high or too low for the average voices of boys and girls. Of course all the tunes were made up (and probably added to afterwards) by people who lived long ago, but each musical arrangement is an original setting by Mr. Stringham.

As for the pictures that adorn the book, I asked Elizabeth Black Carmer to make them, and she has given us here her imaginings of how some of the heroes of the American past looked when they were busy doing the things they did.

Now that stories and songs and pictures are all together in one book we are hoping that many American boys and girls will find in it the feeling that made ours a great land when it, too, was growing. We also hope that the book may add to their knowledge of American geography and history as they read stories and sing songs that give some ideas as to where and when we grew up as a working nation. Finally we hope that by reading these tales and singing these tunes American boys and girls may come somehow to identify themselves with the strong and good who were the pioneers of the early days of America.

Mr. Sims and Henry

Mr. Sims and Henry

OF ALL THE MATES on the stubby, smelly vessels that carried whale oil for American candles across the seas of the world to the shores of Nantucket, Mr. Sims was most famous.

Sailors used to tell many stories about Mr. Sims. They said that in his early days he had shipped aboard a whaler, but had grown tired of standing watch every day for the big spouters of the deep only to have his over-cautious captain, Zebediah Simmons, refuse to let him lower the small boats at the cry of "Thar she blows!" because the wind was too peart.

After the famous voyage on which he finally told Captain Simmons what he thought of him, Mr. Sims went home and did some thinking. Then he went out fishing alone in a dory and returned at sunset with but one catch—a tiny swordfish swimming around lively in a bucket of sea water.

For weeks thereafter Mr. Sims spent every day on the shore training that swordfish, whom he called Henry, to kill and bring back other fish. At first the little fish worked in a thread-line harness, but as time went on he became so fond of Ezekiel Macy Sims (that

[14]

was Mr. Sims's full name) that he gladly swam back home with his catch strung on the end of the long jagged sword that was his nose. Mr. Sims rowed out to the Gloucester Banks one day, with Henry tagging along, and had a hard row home because he hated to throw overboard any of the codfish that were piled up high above the gunwales—each one punctured with a neat round sword-hole.

When Henry grew bigger, Mr. Sims sent him out against bigger and bigger fish until finally one hot afternoon, all of his own accord, he attacked and brought in a shark bigger than Mr. Sims himself.

About a year later folks all up and down the east coast of the United States were laughing heartily at Ezekiel Macy Sims because he had set out in his own whaler, the *Elvira Q. Starbuck* (bought with profits from the sale of fish Henry had caught for him) and had taken no harpoons with him. He just said he had found a way to catch whales without using harpoons and would not talk about it. He had a hard time getting a crew because so many people thought he was crazy, but he did not seem to mind. He said he could get along short-handed with his new method of whale-catching. Some of the crew who did sign for the voyage deserted him when he had the rain water cistern moved from the top of his house, moored to the mainmast, and filled with sea water. They did not know he was just fixing comfortable quarters for Henry.

Naturally, the home folks at Newburyport thought Captain

Sims and Henry would be gone for many months and they were almighty surprised when they saw the *Elvira Q. Starbuck* putting into harbor and riding low in the water just a few weeks later.

Captain Sims retired from following the sea after that voyage. He sold the whale oil aboard for more than a hundred thousand dollars, built himself a big, new house at Newburyport, and sat out the rest of his years. When folks asked him how he got a shipload of oil without even a harpoon he sighed and shook his head a bit before he answered.

He said he did not have to order his men to stand watch for whales. All that was necessary was to take Henry out of the cistern and flip him overboard, then follow in his wake. Henry just naturally had a nose for whales. In a little while he would come upon a big blower who was breathing and belching as well. At once he would run it through with his sword and after the great beast had died of the wound, Henry would swim back to the *Elvira Q. Starbuck*, pushing his victim ahead of him.

If only Henry had not gone after the last whale all would have been well and Captain Sims and he could have gone on many another voyage together. Unhappily the Captain had been so anxious to have a full hold that he had said to Henry as he turned him loose for the final catch,

"Get a big one this time, Henry."

[16]

And Henry, always anxious to please, had rushed upon the biggest whale in the Atlantic, pierced its side with his long sword and in the excitement of the moment lifted it clear of the water. There had been a sharp cracking sound and Henry's sword, under the overpowering weight of the mighty monster, had broken off close to his head.

Gamely Henry had pushed the whale back to Captain Sims, who joyfully lowered the tackle to lift his prize to the deck. Only then did he realize what a tragedy had occurred. That was why, said Captain Sims, he had retired from the sea in sorrow. It explained, too, why, on the flat roof of his handsome Newburyport home there stood an elegantly carved marble bathtub of huge proportions in which, swimming happily about, dwelt the only pug-nosed swordfish in the world. Lastly, it explained why, on clear summer nights in Newburyport, people passing by Captain Sims's fine house used to hear a song that seemed to be coming from high above them. The song was the *Boston Come-All-Ye*, and the Captain was singing it to Henry to console him for the loss of his sword.

Try to sing it as if Henry were listening to you from his lofty marble bathtub.

BOSTON COME ALL-YE

Come, all ye young sail - or men, lis - ten to me, I'll sing you a song of the fish of the sea.

Chorus

Then blow ye winds west - er - ly,

west - er - ly blow, — We're bound to the south'-ard, so stead - y she goes!

Oh, first came the whale, the biggest of all;
He climbed up aloft and let every sail fall.

And next came the mack'rel with his stripèd back;
He hauled aft the sheets and he boarded each tack.

Then came the big porpoise and with his short snout,
He went to the wheel, calling "Ready! About!"

Then came the bold smelt, the smallest of all;
He jumped to the bridge and sang out "Topsail, haul!"

The herring came saying, "I'm king of the seas,
If you want a wind, I will blow you a breeze."

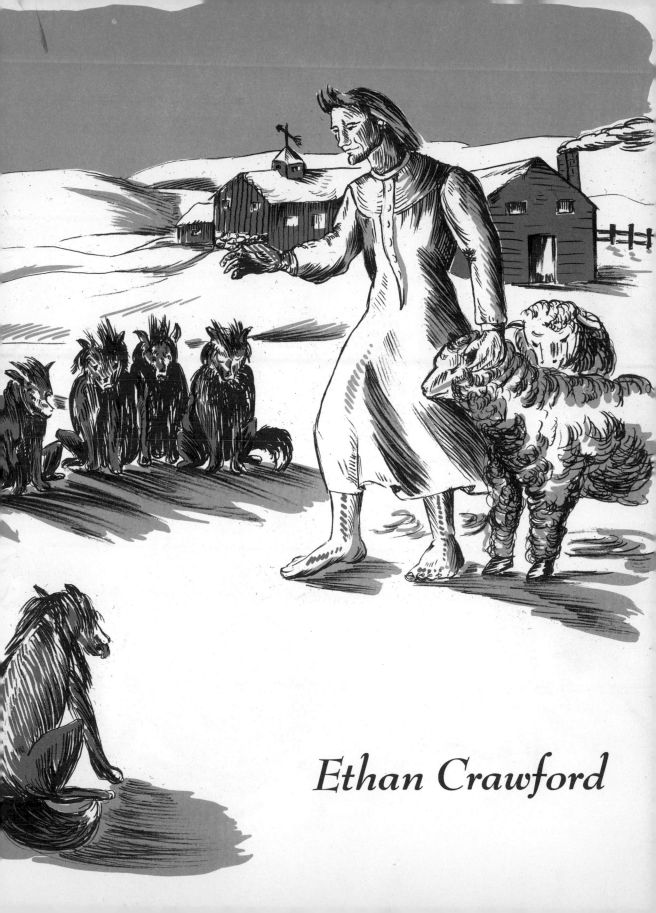

Ethan Crawford

Ethan Crawford

BIG MEN AND STRONG MEN live in the mountains of New England, but folks say that the biggest and the strongest in all Yankee history was Ethan Crawford. Until Ethan was thirteen years old, he never owned a pair of shoes, or a pair of mittens, or even a cap. Though his hands, feet, and head were bare all winter, he could harness and unharness a horse even on the coldest days without having to blow on his fingers to make them warm. Apparently a life of such hardship agreed with him for, by the time he was eighteen years old, he was seven feet tall, the biggest eighteen-year-old in all New England.

Ethan of the Hills lived alone in the wilderness at the foot of Mount Washington. He was so strong that people say he could bear a whole wagonload of hay on his back. He used to wrestle with full-grown bears, they say, and whenever he threw one to the ground, he jumped on him and tied his jaws together before dragging him home to tame him and train him to dance for his food and lodging.

Ethan's fiercest enemies were the wildcats, and they could not be tamed. Folks who live in Crawford's Notch today still tell of the time he saw a wildcat crouching on the limb of a hickory tree and making ready to spring on him. Quickly Ethan made a lasso out of birch sticks, threw it around the neck of the animal and jerked it down within his reach. The cat fought savagely and Ethan's clothes were torn and his hands were scratched, but he finally succeeded in tying the four murderous claws together and carrying the snarler home like a sack of potatoes.

Ethan of the Hills always had more trouble with the New Hampshire wolves than with other animals. In the winter they would come out of the forest suddenly and steal Ethan's sheep. All the fences that Ethan built could not keep the wolves out. Finally Ethan told his sheep that when the wolves came, they should run quickly to the yard in front of his house.

One cold December night a pack of wolves came sneaking out of the forest and the obedient sheep ran to the yard for safety. Their cries for help awakened Ethan and he got up and ran out into the snow in his white nightshirt. He stood in the bright moonlight facing the wolves, and he began to speak to them. They were all so surprised at this that they sat around on their haunches and listened. Ethan preached to them a long and powerful sermon about the wickedness of stealing and the meanness of frightening poor little sheep. The wolves felt more and more ashamed as they listened to him—and when he finished they all hung their heads and walked away. Ethan stood still in the moonlight and watched them go. Just before they reached the forest they stopped, and four of them sang a last, lonely song for Ethan before they disappeared into the darkness forever. It was a song that Ethan and all his neighbors knew very well, for it was called *New England*, and New Hampshire is one of the loveliest states of that region.

As you sing it, try to make the song sound better than it did to Ethan Crawford on the night the wolves' quartet sang it to him.

NEW ENGLAND, NEW ENGLAND

Moderately fast

New Eng-land, New Eng-land, my home by the

sea, My heart as I wan-der turns fond - ly to

thee; For bright rests the sun on thy clear wind-ing

streams, And soft o'er thy mead-ows the moon pours her

beams. New Eng-land, New Eng-land, my home by the sea;___ The wan-der-er's heart turns in fond-ness to thee.

Thy breezes are healthful and clear are thy rills,
The harvest waves proudly and rich on thy hills;
Thy maidens are fair and thy heroes are strong,
Thy rivers run blithely thy valleys among.
New England, New England, my home by the sea,
The wanderer's heart turns in fondness to thee.

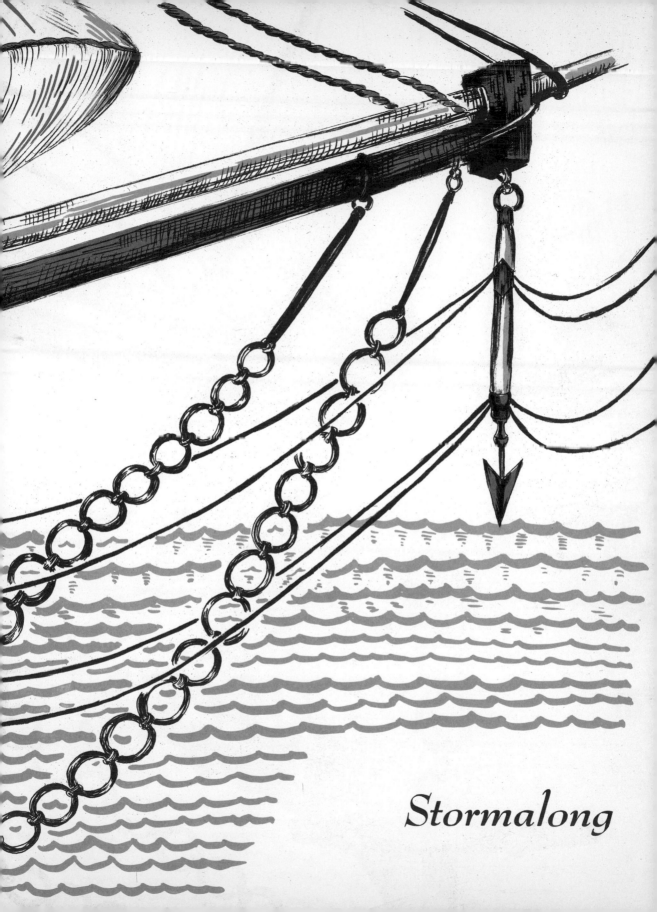

Stormalong

Stormalong

THE FOLKS WHO LIVED along the New England coast in the stretch between Cape Cod and Cape Ann all knew about Alfred Bulltop Stormalong. He was the wonder of that salty region from the day he was born—for he was even then so big that his parents had to commandeer the stout-ribbed framework of a whaler they were building, yank her down off the ways, and line her with six mainsails in order to make a cradle for the child.

Alfred Bulltop Stormalong started outgrowing his cradle at once. By the time he was ten he had already made six voyages as cabin boy and no captain would ship him again because he was too big for any cabin and ate more than any three able seamen. Everybody liked "Stormy" though, for he was smart and he had a very obliging disposition. They remembered the time when a tarnation big octopus had satcheled on to the anchor of the *Dudley Q. Bess* and no amount of heaving by the crew of that good whaleship would bring it up from the bottom. Down went Stormy, hand over hand along the anchor-chain, and pretty soon the sea began to look as though a volcano had erupted below. When the water finally grew calm again, up came Stormy, marching along the anchor-chain, hand over hand.

"I'm glad the second mate taught me how to tie all those different kinds of sailor knots," he said. "That octopus is going to have a hard time getting all his arms untied."

All the folks along the coast were mighty happy a few years later when they heard about the new Clipper-ship *Courser*. "That's the ship for Stormy," they shouted. "Now he will not have to stay at home because he is so big!"

For the *Courser* was so large a ship that even Boston Harbor could not hold her. Her masts were so tall that her builders hinged them in the middle to let them down when necessary to keep them from sweeping the sun and the moon out of the sky. The Sahara Desert was the only flat space that was big enough to hold her sails when they were laid out and being sewed. She carried more canvas than could be found in all the circus tents of the world and she carried some of it in strange places. One of her extra sails was called the skyfungarorum and it was set about eighty feet above and a little to the right of the main truck. It looked like a very large kite and it was made fast by a double-running hitch under the binnacle and aft, through the galley to the cook's cat. Other rigging included four topsail yards on the bowsprit with the halyards leading down through a groove in the keel, up through the stern windows and on to the point where they were hitched to the second mate's picture album. Her decks were so large that each sailor standing watch was furnished with a fast horse which he rode lickety-split in order to cover all the territory he was supposed to before he was relieved by a shipmate.

Stormy was so smart that soon after he shipped aboard the *Courser* he had his first mate papers and he might be still sailing the seven seas if a peculiar thing had not happened.

While the *Courser* was in mid-ocean one September day in the 1840's, the worst hurricane in two hundred years blew up and drove her about something remarkable. Twenty-seven men were ordered to the wheel and all of them working together could not keep her on her course. When the big wind had blown itself out no one could tell where he was except Stormy who took one look at the stars and said, "We're southbound in the North Sea. We're too long to turn round and our best chance for deep water and room to breathe is right through the English Channel if we aren't too wide for it."

The closer the *Courser* came to it, the narrower the English Channel looked.

"All hands over to soap the sides!" yelled Stormy. "And soap her extra heavy on the starboard."

Then he took the wheel himself and eased her through. He held her close up against the steep walls of the cliffs of Dover and most of the soap on the starboard side got scraped off on them—making them shiny and white as they are to this day—but the *Courser* slid through and was once more out on the wide Atlantic.

Stormy set her course then for the Gulf of Mexico because he wanted to see the Mexican General Santa Ana who was said to wear the fanciest uniform in the world. He never got his wish, unfortunately, for he breakfasted one fine morning on six big sharks and caught the indigestion and died. The crew sewed him up in the great mainsail of the *Courser* and sang a song for him before they rolled him overboard.

Think of yourself as one of the crew of the greatest and fastest clipper ships of the world as you sing about Stormy.

STORMALONG

Fairly slow ... *Chorus*

Oh, Storm - y's dead an' gone to rest. To m'

Verse

way - ay Storm - a - long! _____ Of

all the sail - ors he was best,

Chorus

Ay, Ay, Ay, Mis - ter Storm - a - long.

STORMALONG

Oh, Stormy's dead an' gone to rest.
To m' way-ay, Stormalong!
Of all the sailors he was best,
Ay, ay, ay, Mister Stormalong.

For fifty years he sailed the seas
To m' way-ay, Stormalong!
In winter storm and summer breeze:
Ay, ay, ay, Mister Stormalong.

And now old Stormy's day is done
To m' way-ay, Stormalong!
We marked the place where he is gone:
Ay, ay, ay, Mister Stormalong.

Ichabod Paddock

Ichabod Paddock

THE STORY GOES that Captain Ichabod Paddock of Nantucket knew the taste of ocean bottom all the way from Boston to Hyorky. Whenever he doubted where his whale-ship lay he ordered the end of the lead soaped before it was heaved overboard. Once it had hit bottom and been drawn back up Captain Paddock would taste the particles sticking to the soap and say "Grand Banks" or "South of Borneo" or some such place and he would be right. Once when he was resting in his bunk the first mate tried to fool him by heaving the lead into the hold which at the time held sand-ballast from Nantucket. When Captain Paddock tasted the end he jumped clean out of bed.

"Great Scott!" he yelled, "Nantucket's been sunk to the bottom. We're right over my Aunt Sukie's rose garden!"

Once, while outward bound and yet in sight of Nantucket, Captain Paddock saw a big bull whale lolling about. Ordering the small boat lowered he took charge himself and stood in the prow. He was very close to the whale when he hurled his sharp harpoon at it. There was a dull clank and the harpoon fell into the sea. Disgustedly he took up the slack in the rope and hauled the weapon aboard. He put all his strength into his second throw. The harpoon split into a hundred pieces. The whale yawned and closed his eyes sleepily, looking quite satisfied with himself.

Impetuously Ichabod Paddock leaped overboard and swam to the whale.

"Do that again," he said softly.

Again the whale opened his mouth and as he did so Captain Paddock up-ended and dove into the beast's innards.

It was dark as a crow's wing at midnight inside and for a time Ichabod swam about aimlessly. Then he saw a long narrow board-walk leading to a spot of yellow light. Immediately he climbed up on the boardwalk and set out toward the distant rays. When nearly there he saw the light came from the window of a one-room cottage. He knocked softly on the door and a sweet voice said, "Come in."

The room inside was fixed up like a captain's cabin with maps of the South Seas on the walls and a medicine chest in one corner, but the owner of the voice did not look like a sea-going man. In fact Ichabod saw, seated in the center of the room on a carved Chinese chair, a beautiful lady dressed in Oriental silks and holding a stringed musical instrument.

If Ichabod had been an older man he would have known his danger. Every good sea-captain knows that a red-haired woman met inside a whale is a singing witch and must not be listened to. But Ichabod had not been a captain long and did not know about such things.

Outside on the sea, however, Ichabod's friends were trying to save him. His first mate, Elijah Coffin, had seen him dive into the whale and leaping overboard he had swum to Ichabod's boat and climbed aboard. As he did so he heard faint music. Realizing the danger, he set out to row to Nantucket as fast as he could.

When Elijah reached shore he ran to the high square house of Tristram Starbuck. Tristram's girl, Patience, would know what to do. Nantucket folks used to say when they got into a dither, "Patience Starbuck will know what to do." And Patience always knew.

When Patience heard Elijah's breathless story, she began walking swiftly up and down. "It will cost me my great-grandmother's silver tea set," she said, "but better to lose that than leave a poor human soul in the clutches of a witch. Silver is the only metal that will hurt a witch."

Then she made a fire below the big Starbuck oven and inside the oven, in an iron kettle, she put the old tea set. Soon the kettle was nearly full of melted silver. Elijah went to work, then, molding it into a harpoon and as soon as it had hardened Patience covered it with sticky tar to keep the silver from showing.

Swiftly they both ran to Ichabod's boat and set out. When they came to the big whale they heard music.

"Ichabod," called Elijah, "Patience Starbuck is here and says you couldn't tell the taste of bottom off her Aunt Tabitha's dock if it was paved with huckleberry chowder."

The music stopped inside the whale and they heard Ichabod's voice saying, "Excuse me just a minute."

"Don't go," said a voice like the distant hum of a line-squall coming up against the wind.

"Just a minute," said Ichabod firmly, and his friends outside heard a door close. A moment later the whale's mouth opened and there between his white teeth stood Ichabod.

"You can't tell where we fetched up this bottom," said Patience, holding out a soaped lead to which clung bits of seaweed and gravel.

For answer Ichabod dove from the whale's mouth and swam to the boat. Just as he clambered aboard Elijah hurled the silver harpoon at the whale.

"It's no use," said Ichabod; but to his utter amazement the harpoon sank deep.

With a look of pained surprise the whale thrashed about, nearly capsizing the little boat. Some people say that in the next few days he took Patience and Elijah and Ichabod on the longest "Nantucket sleigh-ride" ever taken—north to the shores of Greenland and south to the tropic of Capricorn. On his way back up he tuckered out and finally gave up the ghost right in the lea of Nantucket Island. Patience and Ichabod and Elijah cut him up and took hundreds of barrels of oil from him. They sold it for enough money to buy a tall Nantucket house where they lived out their lives. Ichabod never mentioned the lady whose song had bewitched him and Patience never said anything about the silver harpoon. When they thought about such things they both felt sort of foolish. But whenever Patience had gone to town to do her shopping Ichabod sang the song the red-headed lady taught him inside the whale.

Sing it as if you had learned it the same way.

BLOW, BOYS, BLOW

Gaily swinging

Blow, my boys, I long to hear you,

Blow, boys, blow!

Blow, my boys, I come to cheer you,

Blow, my bul - ly boys, blow!

BLOW, BOYS, BLOW

Blow, my boys, I long to hear you,
    Blow, boys, blow!
Blow, my boys, I come to cheer you,
    Blow, my bully boys, blow!

Yankee ship's gone down the river,
    Blow, boys, blow!
What d'you think they got for dinner?
    Blow, my bully boys, blow!

John Augustus Caesar Darling

WHEN JOHN AUGUSTUS CAESAR DARLING was only a small boy of eleven or so he began to show that he could make up his mind in record time. In two jerks of a lamb's tail, in a jiffy, before you could say "Jack Robinson," in no time at all—there would be the mind of John Augustus Caesar Darling all made up and tied around with a woolen string.

The first time that his parents and neighbors noticed John's especial ability was on an April morning when the boy was out plowing the field his father called "the lower forty" with the family's span of two pet steers. "Plow a straight furrow, John," Mr. Darling said early that morning when his son started out.

"Yes, Father," said John and the older man had gone back to sleep contentedly.

It was ten o'clock and John had been plowing for six hours when he had to make up his mind quickly. Suddenly a seven-foot stump was standing directly in the path of his plow. A boy who was less obedient than John would have shouted "gee" or perhaps "haw" to his steers and swerved around the stump. But John remembered what his father had said. The only way to plow a straight furrow was to go straight ahead.

"Git up, there," he said to the steers.

The sharp edge of the plow hit the stump plumb in the middle and split it fairly in two. "Git up!" shouted John again hurrying through the crack he had made. But the stump was springing back together again. Quickly John lunged forward to avoid being crushed. The two sides met with a loud crack. John had got through between them but his shirt tail, fluttering in the wind, had been fairly caught. Before he could stop his charging steers his shirt had been torn right off his back.

When John Darling became a grown man his beard grew so rapidly that he gave up the idea of being shaved every day and was shaved only once a year. And since he had as fine a stand of hard maples as you could find in all of New York State, he made great use of the maple syrup his trees furnished him. On the first day of summer in each year he would walk to town, carefully avoiding trampling on his beard, and have his barber shave off every whisker. When he had been shaved John would pack the whiskers lying in windrows on the floor into gunny sacks and take them home to his wife who would boil the maple syrup out of them. On years when the buckwheat crop had been a good one and pancakes had been numerous, she used to save as many as ten gallons of syrup that had dripped into John's beard during the winter and spring.

The finest example of John's spryness at making up his mind came in the spring of a year not so long ago. The sap was running early and strong and John had taken his medium-size sap pan which weighed only a ton or so down to the sugarbush with him. He was about to empty the brimming pails that hung below the spouts on his trees into the pan when he heard a loud humming noise and saw in the air above him three Jersey Mosquitoes as big as army bombers. They had spotted John and were circling about making ready to dive on him. Here was a problem in making up his mind quickly that tested even John's swiftness. As the first mosquito started to drop upon him John tipped the big sap pan up on end and let it fall over him, leaving him, as he thought, safely protected in an iron-walled shelter. But his safety did not last long. He could hear the borers of the three mosquitoes hard at work on the outside of the pan. Soon one of them broke through, then another, then the third, and each one was moving about searching for him. Once more John made up his mind in a flash. Seizing his axe which he carried stuck in his belt, he split each borer into two parts and pressed each part back against the wall of the pan. Now the mosquitoes could not reach him nor could they withdraw their borers. For some time, not being able to make up their minds as quickly as John, they buzzed angrily. Then their wings began to whir and in a moment they were in the air, carrying the big sap pan with them. The last John saw of the pan, the mosquitoes were carrying it south toward Jersey flying high above the wooded banks of the Susquehanna River.

John hated to lose the pan but he felt so happy over having made up his mind faster than the Jersey Mosquitoes (who are famous for making up their minds swiftly) that he began to sing a song about making maple syrup and maple sugar which all good sugarbush people have been singing for a long time.

Join in with John and celebrate your own ability to make up your mind quickly with loud singing.

The song is called *Maple Sweet* and these are the words:

When you see the vapor pillar lick the forest and the sky,
You may know the days of sugar making then are drawing nigh;
Frosty night and sunny day, make the maple pulses play,
Till the overflow of sweetness just begins to drip away.

Chorus
　Oh! Bubble, bubble, bubble, bubble goes the pan,
　Furnish sweeter music for the season if you can,
　See the golden billows, watch their ebb and flow
　Sweetest joys indeed, we sugar makers know.

When you see the farmer trudging with the dripping buckets home,
You may know the days of sugar making then have fully come;
As the fragrant odors pour through the open kitchen door,
How the eager children rally, ever loudly calling, "More!"

Do you say you don't believe it? Take a saucer and a spoon
Though you're sourer than a lemon, you'll be sweeter very soon.
Why, the greenest leaves you see, on the spreading maple tree,
Though they sip and sip all summer, will the autumn beauties be.

And for home or love, or any kind of sickness, 'tis the thing,
Take in plentiful doses and repeat it every spring;
Until every one you meet, if at home or on the street,
Will be half a mind to bite you, for you look so very sweet.

[49]

MAPLE SWEET

In a lively patter

Chorus: Oh! Bub - ble, bub - ble, bub - ble, bub - ble,

bub - ble goes the pan,

Fur - nish sweet - er mu - sic for the

sea - son if you can,

See the gold – en bil – lows, watch their ebb and flow, Sweet – est joys in deed, we sug – ar mak – ers know.

Philetus Bumpus

Philetus Bumpus

PHILETUS BUMPUS in his fiery prime couldn't stay still long enough to receive visitors, and so he became captain of the prettiest canal-packet between Albany and Buffalo—the *Bathsheba C. Onderdonck*. Drivers who remembered him used to say that when the mules had plodded along the towpath until they had passed a wooden span across the Erie, Philetus never ducked his head at the cry of "Low Bridge! Everybody down!" He'd walk to the back of the boat and stand upright until it looked as if he was going to get his brains knocked out. Then he'd jump right over the bridge and come down up forward near the staple to which the towrope was hitched.

The event that made Philetus into a dignified and rest-loving citizen happened one day when he was about fifty and piloting a group of distinguished and refined ladies and gentlemen from Lockport to Rochester. It was a lovely day. White clouds drifted above green fields and the ladies and gentlemen seated on the deck exchanged polite remarks on the beauties of nature, as the mules dragged the big boat slowly eastward.

All would have been well if a Hudson River sturgeon on his way to visit cousins in Lake Erie had not noted in passing the anchor of the *Bathsheba C. Onderdonck* hanging neatly at her stern. Apparently the sturgeon was near-sighted and mistook the anchor either for an outsize angleworm or possibly one of those tangles of baked salt dough known as pretzels.

At any rate he made a grab for it and set out for Buffalo. Captain Bumpus and all his passengers felt a sudden jerk. The next thing they knew they were traveling back over the way they had come at a much faster speed than that to which they were accustomed, and the mules had developed with startling ease the ability to run backwards. The *Bathsheba C. Onderdonck* flashed through Rochester stern-first and by the time she reached Spencerport she was leaving so great a swell in her wake that the hired men working on the farms beside the canal later claimed they had seen a tidal wave.

The *Bathsheba C. Onderdonck* streaked it through Adam's Basin and Albion and Eagle Harbor, through Medina and Middleport. When the sturgeon reached Lockport the big locks had been filled to let a boat go through and the lock-keeper had just opened the doors to release the water. The big fish squirmed up that hill of water so fast it had no time to run out and the *Bathsheba C. Onderdonck* went right along.

All this time Captain Philetus Bumpus had been standing guard over the taut anchor rope, for indignant passengers were determined to cut it and this would make him lose his anchor. As the boat was backing through Buffalo, a frightened mother held up her little girl-baby to his stern gaze and begged him for the sake of the children aboard to cut the rope before they were all dragged into the depths of stormy Lake Erie. Only then, with a tear in his eye, did Philetus raise his axe and cut the rope.

The whole experience so unnerved him that he retired from following the canal and became a tavern keeper at Albion. He sold his mules to a little traveling circus that came through Orleans County one day, and for many years they delighted circus crowds by galloping backwards as they learned to do when the sturgeon had them in tow. The tavern was loved by all canalers and on many a summer night a fleet of boats would be tied up outside, while drivers and owners joined Captain Philetus Bumpus in singing the most famous of all Erie Canal songs.

Suppose we join the group and sing with them. You'll have to sing very loudly to hear your own voice.

LOW BRIDGE, EVERYBODY DOWN

al-ways tell your neigh-bor, you can al-ways tell your pal, If you've

ev - er nav - i - ga - ted on the E - rie Ca - nal. *sfz*

We've hauled some barges in the good old day,
Filled with coal and barley and hay—
Most every inch of every mile I know
From Albany to Buffalo!

We'd better look now for a job, Old Pal,
Fifteen years on the Erie Canal,
You bet your life I wouldn't part with Sal,
Fifteen years on the Erie Canal.

So get on, Pal, we've got to pass that lock,
We'll make Rome 'fore it's six o'clock,
So one more trip and on our way we'll go
Right straight back to Buffalo.

Chorus

Low bridge, everybody down,
Low bridge, I've the finest mule in town.
Eats a bale of hay for dinner, and on top of that my Sal
Tries to drink up all the water in the Erie Canal.

Phillip Babb

Phillip Babb

LONG YEARS BEFORE the American Revolution a band of Irish men and women left their homes to go to America. Far across the Atlantic among the hills of New England lay the village of Londonderry which had been named after an Irish town they loved and they knew that they would find old friends there. In the good ship *Wolf* they sailed for many weeks and they were happy because their long voyage would soon be at an end.

When they were not far from Boston harbor there came a day of fair weather and little wind, and suddenly on the horizon the lookout saw a dark and rakish schooner bearing down rapidly upon the *Wolf*. As it came nearer the passengers saw that she flew no flag and there were cannon on her deck. "Perhaps she is a pirate ship," they said, and they were silent with dread.

Suddenly a cannonball skipped the waves just beyond the prow of the *Wolf* and the sound of the big gun echoed through the still air.

"Heave to!" cried the captain and he called all the passengers together and said, "We are unarmed and helpless. We will have to await what comes, bravely."

A small boat put out from the schooner and the passengers of the *Wolf* could see the grim, sunburned men at the oars. Soon they were climbing aboard. The last man to come over the side was dark and sturdy. By his fine clothes and his shining sword the passengers knew he must be Phillip Babb, the captain. Threateningly, he advanced upon them. "Bind them and throw them into the sea," he said to his men.

Even as he spoke a tiny cry came from below—the frightened wail of a baby. Phillip Babb hesitated. "Bring the mother and child to me," he said.

Soon up from a hatchway came a beautiful young woman bearing in her arms a very new baby that had been born on the voyage. The child was pleased by the sunlight and stopped crying to gurgle and smile.

"Is your child a boy or girl?" asked the captain.

"A girl."

"Has she a name?"

Fearfully the young woman shook her head.

"Not yet," she said.

"If you will name her Mary after my own good mother," said the swarthy captain, "I will spare you and all the rest."

"I will do so," said the young woman joyfully.

Then the pirate captain ordered his men to return to their ship. "Do not continue on your course," he said to the captain of the *Wolf*, "until I have come back with a gift for my dear mother's new namesake."

In a little while the pirates had rowed their captain back to his ship and were returning. They laughed as they rowed and they cheered when Phillip Babb once more boarded the *Wolf* where the mother and the new baby waited. This time he carried in his arms a roll of gray-green satin on which pink blossoms had been exquisitely embroidered.

"It is for little Mary's wedding dress," he said, giving it to the baby's mother.

Twenty years later a tall and lovely bride, known to all her friends as Ocean-born Mary, was married to a strong and handsome young man in Londonderry, New Hampshire.

As she stood beside her husband she thought of the strange happenings that had brought to her the material of her lovely wedding dress long ago. And when her own babies came in the course of time—three fine boys who grew up to be brave soldiers in the war for American Independence—she used to sing them a song her mother had sung to her in the days after the pirate captain had given her the beautiful gray-green cloth.

Sing it as if you were singing it with Ocean-born Mary—to
her three little boys.

A SHIP A-SAILING

I saw a ship a-sailing, a-sailing on the sea,
And it was deeply laden with pretty things for me.
There was candy in the cabin and almonds in the hold;
The sails were made of bright red silk and the mast
    was made of gold.

The four and twenty sailors that stood between the decks
Were four and twenty white mice with rings about their necks.
The captain was a duck, a duck, with a jacket on his back;
And when this fairy ship set sail, the captain said,
    "Quack, quack."

A SHIP A-SAILING

With a slow, rocking swing

I saw a ship a - sail - ing, a -

sail - ing on the sea, _____ And

it was deep - ly lad - en with

pret - ty things for me. _____ There was

candy in the cab - in and al - monds in the hold; ____ The sails were made of bright red silk and the mast was made of gold.

Anthony the Trumpeter

Anthony the Trumpeter

In the little thick-walled stone houses that still stand on the banks of the Hudson River mothers are telling their children even to this day about Anthony the Trumpeter.

Anthony was born in Holland but his father and mother brought him to the mouth of the Hudson when he was a small boy. There, in the little town of New Amsterdam which is now the big city of New York, little Anthony grew to be big Anthony. He wanted to be big because then there would be room for much air inside him and he wanted to hold much air so that he could play the trumpet loudly and well. So Anthony ate and drank a great deal and his body grew big and round as a barrel and there was almost as much room for air in it.

Anthony's only regret was that as he came to have more and more the shape of a man who could blow a big horn well, his nose kept growing larger and redder and more and more shiny. He felt a little ashamed of this until one day he went for a sail up the Hudson with many companions. He was standing at the prow of the gay sloop that was bearing the party northward through the beautiful hills beside the river, when a hot ray of the sun struck his nose and was reflected so strongly from the red and shiny surface that it struck downward and killed a large sturgeon that was slowly swimming by. Anthony's friends pulled the big fish aboard and discovered that it had not only been killed by the ray but thoroughly cooked as well, and the whole party feasted. After that Anthony was proud of his nose, for his friends insisted on naming the high steep hill which they were passing at the time of the event "Anthony's Nose"—and Anthony's Nose it is, even to this day.

When Anthony was big enough and strong enough to blow the kind of a horn he wanted to buy, he bought a trumpet of shining brass. It did not take him long to learn to play it, though some of his neighbors said it *seemed* like a very long time. In a few weeks he blew so loudly and so well that he became the official trumpeter for New Amsterdam and frequently he walked before the governor of the colony and blew loud notes announcing his coming.

At first some of Anthony's companions laughed at him because he was so round and fat but their laughing soon stopped when they found out that Anthony was a brave man and a smart one. A band of Indians attacked New Amsterdam one day and Anthony, blowing the charge, dashed in among the foe. Finding himself quite alone and surrounded by painted savages, he put his talent to use and blew such a blast that every Indian standing nearby was made deaf by the noise. Frightened by their sudden deafness the savages rushed away, followed by the rest of the tribe. Thus Anthony saved the little city from capture by Indians and the townspeople gave him a great feast at which his nose shone large and red and round as a full moon at harvest time.

The bravest thing that Anthony the Trumpeter ever did was the last act of his life. When the British fleet came to capture New Amsterdam and take it away from Dutch rule, Governor Peter Stuyvesant ran as fast as his wooden peg leg would let him to the home of Anthony the Trumpeter.

"Go and tell the good Dutch people up the river what a fearful thing has happened," said Peter, and Anthony obediently set out, though darkness was falling and a fierce storm was about to break.

By the time that Anthony came to the Harlem River, which separates Manhattan Island from the mainland of North America, lightning was flashing through the black sky and a heavy wind was blowing. The ferryboat that usually took people across the stream was nowhere to be seen.

"I will cross this river in spite of the devil," said Anthony, shaking an angry fist, and as he did so thunder roared around him.

Into the black and rolling stream he plunged, his gleaming brass trumpet held out of the water while he kicked mightily with his feet. He had gone perhaps half the way across when a fearful sea serpent rose to the surface of the water and grabbed him. By the lightning's flare Anthony could see the long coils of the serpent's body and his strange head from which three sets of eyes glared in as many directions. Its head was grown over by a mane, like that of a lion, and from his snout grew a tusk eight feet long. From between his four sets of teeth came a mighty snarl and from his nostrils went up spouts of hot steam. Anthony could smell sulphur all about him and he could see the green banks where the monster had lain, all scorched and brown. Bravely he struggled with the awful beast and finally, freeing his right arm, he raised his trumpet to his lips and blew so mighty a blast that farmers along the banks of the Hudson claimed that they heard it as far north as Pough-keepsie and were warned of danger.

The loud note ended in a bubbling sound as the serpent dragged Anthony the Trumpeter down into the water, never again to be seen. But after that, Dutch mothers told their children how brave and good Anthony was to lose his life trying to protect his friends and their families. He died, they said, so that mothers and babies might live in peace beside the great River-of-the-Mountains —as some people call the Hudson. And then they took their youngest children in their arms and sang them a lullaby that was an old lullaby when Anthony the Trumpeter was a little boy. Let us sing it, not too loudly, so that soon the baby will be asleep.

DUTCH LULLABY

A DUTCH LULLABY

Sleep, little one, sleep!
Out of doors there runs a sheep!
A sheep with four white feet,
That drinks its milk so sweet,
Sleep, baby, sleep!

Sleep, little one, sleep!
Out of doors there runs a sheep!
In the fields there runs a spotted cow,
Its calf has shut its eyelids, so
Sleep, baby, sleep!

Oregon Smith

Oregon Smith

OREGON SMITH LIVED in Bloomington, Indiana, all his life except for one trip to the state he was named after. After he came back from the wonderful land beyond the Rockies, people used to crowd around Oregon no matter where he was, and ask him to tell them stories of his journey. Some of them used to say they did not believe the tales Oregon told them but he always answered them by saying, "You weren't with me—so how do you know I'm lying?"

Oregon said that in the land he was named after apples grew to the size of Indiana pumpkins and as for the pumpkins, they grew so big in the Rogue River Valley in Oregon that he had once cut a hole through one and then driven a coach and four horses through it. He said that in Oregon, even when it rained, nobody ever got wet for the rain was dry and smelled a lot like the sachet powder in his aunt's bureau drawer.

Nobody did much coon hunting out in that country, Oregon said, because the coon-dogs were so active and intelligent that when they were let out they would not only tree a coon at once but climb the tree, kill the coon, and drag him home to be skinned. When he was making a needed fur coat out of coonskins he owned a dog so smart that he would tree coons with skins of just the right size for completing the garment. Unfortunately, on an occasion when he was describing a bear he had shot lately to some of his friends, the dog got the idea from his gestures that he wanted a coonskin that big and went out to find one. He never came back.

One of the most interesting of Oregon Smith's statements about Oregon was that no one in the state ever made butter. If a family needed butter, they just set nets for it in the John Day River. When he was asked to explain this remark Oregon used to say that herds of buffalo cows up in the mountains liked to stand belly-deep in the lively whirlpools up near the source of the river. The swirling water not only drew the milk from their udders but churned it as well, causing blobs of butter to float downstream.

Telling these stories about his western visit gradually came to be Oregon Smith's life work. He began thinking that other folks should do his work for him and take care of him in return for his accounts of what happened to him out in Oregon. Little by little he gave up doing his work in the fields and in the home. Finally he decided it was too much trouble to dress, and so he lay in bed all day just talking about Oregon. For some years he lay without moving a muscle except the one that kept his jaws going.

One day Oregon Smith's brother-in-law with whom he had gone to live just before he took to his bed, said to him,

"You might as well be dead."

"Don't interrupt me," said Oregon impatiently—"What was that you said?"

"I remarked that you might as well be dead. We all know those stories by heart and all you do is tell 'em. If we buried you you'd be out of the way and you wouldn't be eatin' us out of house and home. In fact, I'm suggesting that you either get up and go to work or we *will* bury you."

"Bury away!" said Oregon. "I ain't worked in so long I don't believe my hand would be in, anyway."

So Oregon's brother-in-law rigged up a board coffin and laid Oregon in it. Then he put the whole kit and kaboodle into his wagon, clucked to the horses, and started for the cemetery.

But one of Oregon's kind Indiana neighbors had heard about the plan his brother-in-law had made, and felt sorry about it. He dumped a half-dozen bushels of good roastin'-ears into his own wagon and set out to meet Oregon going to his own funeral.

"Oregon," he said when he'd got Oregon's brother-in-law to pull up beside the road, "I hear this stingy near-relative of yours is going to bury you because he grudges you your victuals. So I brought you this sweet-corn to eat and you can live on my place in that old cabin next to the barn. Ought to last you a long time if you are sparing of it—and when that's gone the Ladies' Aid Society say they'll see that you get fed. How about it?"

"Neighbor," said Oregon, "that's mighty nice of you, but I want to ask you a question—is that sweet-corn shucked?"

"Why, no," said the neighbor, "it's not."

"Drive on, brother," said Oregon. "Now, as I was sayin'—out in Seattle—we used to sing a song about a feller that felt about work jest about the same as me."

Then, as the wagon rolled on, he began to sing and let's join in with him.

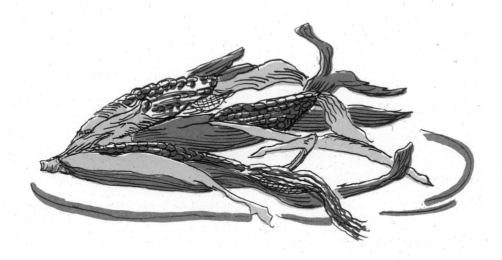

OLD DAN TUCKER

Get out o' the way, Old Dan Tuck-er!

Get out o' the way, Old Dan Tuck-er!

You're too late to get your sup-per.

And next upon the gravel road
I met the gopher and the toad.
And every time the toad would sing,
The gopher cut the pigeon wing.

Mike Fink

Mike Fink

NOBODY HAS EVER figured it out to a standstill whether Mike Fink was a better jumper than a shooter or a better shooter than a jumper. From Pittsburgh to Cairo along the banks of the Ohio River many an evening by the fireside has been spent arguing about it. The arguers who favor Mike's shooting say he could stand on the deck of his keel-boat drifting downriver and shoot the curl out of a baby pig's tail as it rested peacefully against his baby hams in the clear Ohio air. They say he did it so often that to this day there's a breed of Ohio pigs that have straight tails from birth and that this fact is due to Mike's having shot the curls out of the tails of their parents. They also say that Mike used to shoot the top-knots off wild Indians war-whooping among the sycamores on the Indiana bank. Most gracefully, too, he used his bullets to lift the combs out of the carefully done-up tresses of lovely southern ladies as they strolled along the old Kentucky shore.

But the other arguers are just as sure that Mike's real gift was for jumping. They say that when the current was swift he had been known to take off from his forward deck just as his keel-boat neared an island and come down on his after-deck near the sweep at the stern just as the boat left the island behind.

Then some who have heard this tale before shake their heads and say the teller has left out the best part of it—that while Mike was in the middle of his jump over the island a farmer down below took him for a chicken hawk and, lifting his gun, let go at him. Luckily Mike had seen the quick move below and trained his own gun, which he had forgotten to leave behind, on the farmer. Both men fired at the same moment and the two bullets were so well aimed that they met in mid-air and dropped to earth—killing on the way a large black bear that was perched in a honey tree.

Both sides of the argument use the best known of all the Mike Fink jumping stories to prove that they are right, and it is very hard to decide which side wins, for a lot depends on how the tale is told. It all began when Mike bragged that he could jump the Mississippi River at the point where the Ohio comes into it.

"You mean you could take off from Cairo, Illinois, and come down at Birds Point?" said a flat-boatman.

"That's just like a flat-boatman," said Mike, "always belittling the natural gifts of men smart enough to load their stuff into a boat with a sharp edge down the middle."

"If you can do it I'll buy me a keel-boat instead of this broad-horn," said the flat-boatman.

And so, just out of a wish to do something for a man who did not have sense enough to do something for himself, Mike said he would make the try. Saturday was the day set—in order that the school children in Illinois and Kentucky and Missouri could be there. A lot of other folks showed up, too—all the flat-boatmen on the western rivers and all the keel-boatmen and a great many people who were not boatmen at all. The time set for the jump was noon because Mike figured there would be less air stirring then. He would not want to buck a breeze or to hear a flat-boatman say he got blown across. He decided he could get enough of a start by running down Main Street in Cairo and taking off at the foot.

Promptly at noon, when the sun was overhead and the air was still, Mike started his run. He had got under way and was just passing the First National Bank lickety-split when something happened. A little girl, all dressed up in her holiday best and not knowing Mike had started, ran out into the middle of the street. "I can't tell you how I felt at that moment," said Mike later. "Should I keep right on and run her down or should I swerve and break my stride?" All who have experienced the natural courtesy of keel-boatmen know that there could be only one answer. He swerved.

So when Mike came to the foot of Main Street, Cairo, Illinois, he was not running full-tilt as he should have been but he leaped into the air anyway—aiming for Birds Point. The first part of the jump he said later was very pleasant. He could see the river below, lying still and hot, but the breeze caused by his own speed kept him cool and contented. Gradually Cairo got smaller and smaller and he could see the mid-river line where the green Ohio water joins the yellow flood of the Mississippi. Then gradually he began to lose speed. The little girl in his path had caused a bad take-off.

Now he could see the houses of Birds Point getting larger and larger but he knew that he would never reach them. In a few moments he would drop into the river. With a tremendous effort he whirled about in the air and changed the direction of his jump. He was bound back towards Cairo. For a while it seemed as if he would never make it and he shut his eyes and held his nose expecting to fall into the river. When he opened them again the stores of Cairo were but a few rods away. With a last desperate effort he urged himself forward and his right foot lit on dry land. His left foot, landing behind the right, got sopping wet in Mississippi water. That is how close it was.

That famous leap made more argument than ever about Mike Fink's jumping. All the flat-boatmen said they would stick to flat-boats since Mike had failed in his try but all the keel-boatmen pointed out that three quarters of the way over and back is longer than all the way over. Nobody could come to any agreement and so Mike called to his crew and they all set out up the Ohio by catching hold of bushes along the banks and pulling the keel-boat along by them. They called this slow business "bushwhacking" and to while away the time they sang a song that every flat-boatman and keel-boatman on the Ohio used to know.

Sing the first stanza as if you were floating swiftly down stream, the second as if you were bushwhacking back.

SHAWNEE TOWN

Rhythmically and slowly

Hard up-on the beach oar, She moves too slow, _____ All the way to Shaw-nee town, Long time a - go.

SHAWNEE TOWN

Hard upon the beach oar,
She moves too slow;
All the way to Shawnee town,
Long time ago.

Now the river takes her,
We'll get there soon;
Bushwack her back home again,
Under the moon.

Johnny Appleseed

Johnny Appleseed

OF ALL THE STORIES that Americans like to tell about the days of the first plantings of fruit trees in their country, I think they like best the story of a strange fellow who rode into Pittsburgh on the back of a wagon in 1794. He said his name was Jonathan Chapman, and he built himself a log cabin on Grant's Hill.

It's a long time for a story to carry by word of mouth, but there are some people who say he told it around Pittsburgh that he had been born in the state of Massachusetts in the year of the Battle of Bunker Hill and that the first thing his baby eyes ever saw was a branch of appleblossoms outside the window of his home. If that is true, the sight must have influenced the whole rest of his life, for as soon as he had his house built in Pittsburgh he planted a big apple orchard and he bought some hives of bees. There on the hill the bees in Jonathan Chapman's hives made honey from the appleblossoms and Jonathan gave it away to his neighbors because, he said, the bees didn't charge him anything for it.

In the twelve years he lived in Pittsburgh an idea kept growing in Jonathan Chapman's brain. He would take a load of appleseeds westward to the pioneers on the frontier so that they might have flowering, fruitful orchards like his own.

So one day Jonathan loaded two canoes with appleseeds and started down the Ohio River. When he got to the Muskingum he followed that to White Woman Creek, and finally ended up along Licking Creek where his load of seeds ran out. Behind him farmers were rejoicing in their seedlings—soon to be waving orchards—and they talked about the strange man who had brought them. They called him Johnny Appleseed.

Johnny went back to the Pennsylvania cider mills to get more seeds. They're still talking about him around Shadeland and Blooming Valley and Coolspring—the queer, blue-eyed man with long hair hanging to his shoulders, barefooted, wearing ragged clothes. When he had disposed of a second load and come back to Pennsylvania for seeds again, his appearance had changed still more. On his head as a cap he wore a tin kettle in which, when he needed it, he cooked his food. His only garment now, winter or summer, was a coffee sack with holes cut in it for his arms and legs.

Strange stories about him came out of the western wilderness.

Hostile Indians treated Johnny Appleseed kindly and helped him on his way.

A trapper had come upon Johnny Appleseed playing with three bear cubs while their mother looked on placidly.

Johnny Appleseed knew direction by instinct and never carried a compass in the trackless woods.

Johnny Appleseed did not feel the cold of winter and could walk barefoot in below-zero weather without freezing his toes.

Johnny Appleseed had saved the people living in the fort at Mansfield, Ohio, from massacre by Indians, by running sixty miles through the dense woods in five hours to obtain aid.

Hundreds of Ohio acres were abloom with pink blossoms now, and Pennsylvania seeds had reached the banks of the Wabash River. Everywhere Johnny Appleseed was welcomed by the grateful farmers. When he sat down at table with them, he would not eat until he was sure that there was plenty of food for the children. After he had eaten he would stretch himself out on the floor, take out the Bible he carried inside the coffee sack, and read aloud what he called "news fresh from heaven"—the Sermon on the Mount. His voice, one good housewife said, was "loud as the roar of wind and waves, then soft and soothing as the balmy airs that quivered the morning-glory leaves about his gray beard."

One day he trudged along for twenty miles to reach the home of a friend near Fort Wayne, Indiana. He sat down on the doorstep to eat his evening meal of bread and milk. He read aloud from the Bible for a while. Then he went to sleep, stretched out on the floor, and he did not wake up.

When the news reached Washington, old Sam Houston, Texas Sam Houston, made a speech about Johnny Appleseed in the American Congress. He said: "This old man was one of the most useful citizens of the world in his humble way. Farewell, dear old eccentric heart. Your labor has been a labor of love, and generations yet unborn will rise up and call you blessed."

This is just what the farmers who own apple orchards along Johnny Appleseed's path over a territory of a hundred thousand square miles have been doing ever since. And all the folks in western Pennsylvania bless Johnny Appleseed, too, for they know that when Spring comes to the land known now as the Middle West, hundreds of thousands of Ohio and Indiana acres will be pink and white with Pennsylvania appleblossoms.

And today in Indiana, after the apples have been picked from the trees in the orchards, the boys and girls who have helped with the picking like to go to parties and sing a song that was sung in the days of Johnny Appleseed.

They dance as they sing it and I hope you will too.

OLD BRASS WAGON

Cir - cle to the left, the Old Brass Wag-on,

Cir - cle to the left, the Old Brass Wag-on,

Cir-cle to the left, the Old Brass Wag-on,

You're the one, my dar - ling.

OLD BRASS WAGON

1. Circle to the left, the Old Brass Wagon,
   You're the one, my darling.

2. Swing, oh swing around, the Old Brass Wagon,
   You're the one, my darling.

3. Promenade to right, the Old Brass Wagon,
   You're the one, my darling.

4. Walk it up and down, the Old Brass Wagon,
   You're the one, my darling.

5. Break and swing around, the Old Brass Wagon,
   You're the one, my darling.

6. Promenade to right, the Old Brass Wagon,
   You're the one, my darling.

NOTE: Repeat the first line of each stanza three times.

During 1, all join hands, boys being at the left of their partners, and circle left. At 2, they drop hands and each boy swings his partner. During 3, partners promenade, circling to the right. Do what the song tells you while you sing stanzas 4, 5, and 6.

Davy Crockett

Davy Crockett

Davy Crockett went out bear hunting in the state of Arkansas one day and not a single bear showed up to be killed. By sundown Davy was plumb discouraged and he was far away from home on the top of Whangdoodle Knob. Rather than walk home in the dark he decided to spend the night right where he was, so he hung his powderhorn on a little yellow twig, lay down, and dropped off to sleep.

When he waked both the yellow twig and the powderhorn were gone. He searched and searched for them. Then he began asking himself questions.

"Davy," he said to himself, "what did that little yellow twig look like?"

"Well, Davy," he answered, "it was sort of shiny yellow and it was curved like a pine shaving. Maybe it favored a thin slice of butter a little more than a shaving or maybe a new moon."

"Why, you gnat-brained old galoot," said Davy, "why in the name of common sense didn't you say that in the first place? You've been hornswoggled by that little yellow twig, for it *was* the new moon. Now you'll have to wait up here until evening for that sliver of cheese to bring back your powder."

All that day Davy waited. He had no powder to hunt bears with so he went coon hunting, just using his grin to bring the little climbers out of the trees. Time and again a smart old coon looked down to see Davy grinning at him and said, "If that's you, Mr. Crockett, and I can see it is you by your grin, don't you bother to shoot me. I'll come down and climb into your bag all by myself."

Davy had only one slip-up during the day and that was when he mistook a big knot on a branch for a coon and grinned at it. Nothing happened, so Davy grinned again and a lot harder. All the bark flew off the knot and knocked a nearby turkey buzzard galley-west or as some people say—into the middle of next week.

Nobody in America had a more remarkable set of wild animal pets than Davy Crockett. There was his pet alligator, "Long Mississippi" on whose back he once rode up the falls of Niagara, and his pet buffalo, "Mississip," who used to carry the bass in the quartets which Davy was continually getting up in order to sing patriotic airs. And there was "Death Hug," Davy's powerful famous black bear. Death Hug was very fond of sports. He was a fine swimmer, a practically unbeatable wrestler, and one of the fanciest skaters who ever cut a figure eight into the ice of a western river.

Among Davy's best friends was another great skater named

Ben Hardin. Ben was quite jealous of Death Hug's fame and tried his best to outdo him on the ice. One winter day he was skating on the Arkansas river when he saw Davy and Death Hug doing a schottische on their steel runners to the tune of *The Bride's Farewell*.

"Let's all three play," said Ben. "Let's play snap the whip and I'll be the anchor man and we'll see if Death Hug can keep from being snapped off at the end."

Death Hug and Davy agreed and the three started off at breakneck pace. Faster and faster they went. Ben was just getting ready to dig in his heels and stop short in order to send Death Hug full kettle into the bank when a spark struck from Davy's skates found its way into the breech of Davy's gun. There was a terrific explosion and all three skaters found themselves sitting on the ice but still moving as fast as ever. Indeed the speed was so great that although Ben was sliding on a frozen surface, the seat of his breeches at once burned through with the heat of the friction and he began to shout that the ice felt hot beneath him.

Word had gone on ahead of the strange accident that had befallen the three skaters and as they passed Little Rock the whole population of the town was stretched out along the banks of the Arkansas to watch them pass and cheer on their favorites. Little streaks of smoke began to come from the ice as the still seated skaters passed over it. Death Hug was close to the right bank and many folks said afterward that they could smell the odor of burning fur as he passed.

Near Pine Bluff there is a bend in the river and the three piled up on the shore. Those who saw the end of the race all argued that they hit land at exactly the same moment. It was a dead heat, they said, and they agreed that it was the fastest time ever made by three racers in a sitting posture.

After Davy Crockett and Death Hug and Ben Hardin had cooled themselves sufficiently by sitting for an hour or so in a nearby snow bank, all three went to the tavern at Pine Bluff and there Ben sang a song which he said he had composed in memory of his first meeting with Davy Crockett. Old Mississip, the shaggy buffalo, joined in to carry the bass and soon everybody in the place was hard at it. Let's all raise the roof of the tavern at Pine Bluff.

DAVY CROCKETT

Now, don't you ev - er want to know some
things con - cern - ing Where it was I came from and
where I got my learn - ing? Oh, the
world is made of mud out of the
Mis - sis - sip - pi Riv - er! The

sun's a ball of fox fire, as well you may dis-cov-er.

Chorus

Let's go walk-ing out at night, The stars shine bright, They
make the world so light, When the moon is out of sight.

And when one dark and stormy night the moon was mooning,
I met Davy Crockett and he was going cooning,
And I said, "Where is your gun?" And then he said, "I haven't got one,"
"Then how do you kill a coon when you haven't got a gun?"

I then flung down my gun, took off my ammunition,
Said I, "Uncle Davy, I can cool your great ambition."
He threw back his shaggy head and he blew out just like a steamer
Said he, "My boy, you see I'm a Tennessee-born screamer."

Oh, we locked horns and then we wrestled in the thorn
And we had a fight, 'twas the worst since I was born.
For we fought a day and night then we agreed we'd better stop it
For I was pretty well licked—and so was Davy Crockett.

Jim Higgins

Jim Higgins

STANDING AT THE GREAT OAR-SWEEPS of their heavily-laden flat-boat night after night, Jim Higgins and Old Bill Reese had watched the comet of 1811 disappear into unknown skies. By August the wide current of the Mississippi had borne them downriver to New Orleans. Summer was over before they had sold their turkeys and tobacco and the lumber they got from taking the flat-boat apart. Nobody would believe they could get back up the Mississippi, back up the Ohio to Indiana in time to drift another load down before Christmas. They set out walking though, and in six days, according to Jim, they had covered the fifteen hundred miles from New Orleans to home. It took them ten days more to build a flat-boat apiece and get each one filled up with the right sort of cargo. Then, with the stars and stripes fluttering in the Indiana breeze, the two partners gave each craft to the swift current of the Ohio.

For a couple of days the two flatboats raced neck and neck and it was hard to tell which was ahead as they passed the old red brick buildings of Cairo and swung southward with the Mississippi's flood. They were tearing down the broad yellow channel of the Father of Waters when all of a sudden Jim Higgins' boat fetched up kerwallop on a sandbank that was just a smidgeon under water—and there she stuck while Old Bill Reese drifted merrily onward waving his red shirt in farewell.

After Jim Higgins saw that he could not budge his flat-boat and would have to wait for a heavy rain to raise the water and float her off, he decided to go bear hunting. Every morning for a week he swam ashore, holding his rifle and powderhorn out of the water to keep them dry, and every night he swam back without a single bear. He tried the Kentucky shore and he tried the Arkansaw shore and all the bears seemed to have gone somewhere else. By the eighth morning he was almost discouraged but he swam over to Arkansaw and there on the bank drinking up the river was the biggest Arkansaw bear he had ever seen. Indeed, he was such a fine bear that Jim decided not to shoot him but to capture him alive and keep him for a pet.

When the bear saw Jim he made for the nearest tree but Jim scrambled right up after him and there in the lowest branches they fought until they both fell to the ground. Then Jim jumped on the bear and got his favorite wrestling hold on him and the bear knew he would have to give up—so he did. Jim made him swim out to the flat-boat and chained him up with the anchor-chain which he nailed fast with a staple to the forward deck.

There was no more hunting after that. Jim got out his old hemlock fiddle and sat up forward teaching the bear to dance to the music. He played *Mustard Plaster Hurts* and *Granny's Cock-eyed Cat* and *Uncle Wash has Washed his Corn,* and the bear got on amazingly. He learned to cut a neat pigeon-wing at the corners and to jump up and bring his heels together in the air on the prom-enades. Then Jim gave him some harder lessons and played *Fly in* the Buttermilk, *Shoo, Fly, Shoo!* and *Danny in the Cotton Patch* and *Bird in the Cage, He Can't Get Out.* By this time the bear was getting into the spirit of the thing and putting in a little hoe-down in the intermissions between the new figures which Jim had taught him. They were both going great guns on *The Boatman's Dance* when around the bend above them came the strangest sight either of them had ever seen.

For bearing down on them all tricked out in white paint and looking for all the world like a fancy birthday cake on a raft was the first steamboat ever to flutter a wheel on the Mississippi River. Black smoke poured from her twin stacks and she split the water in front of her like a knife through butter in midsummer. On her wheelhouse was painted the name *New Orleans* and she was flying pennants and banners all over her. On her prow surveying the scene as calm as you please stood Mr. Nicholas Roosevelt twiddling his watch chain and smoking a long cigar.

The bear took one look and dove overboard. Jim would have done the same if he had not remembered just in time that water would be bad for his fiddlestrings. While he was considering what to do the steamboat passed him, leaving a wide foaming wake. Just then he felt a tremendous jerk and his flatboat almost went out from under him as she floated free and took out after the steamboat. In practically no time at all she had caught up and the two boats raced side by side for an hour or so. Then the flat-boat began to forge ahead. She was skimming the surface like a sandpiper, riding easy and free. In a little while she passed Old Bill Reese's boat as if she were standing still. So Jim decided to sit back and play his fiddle for a time, while the wind of the swift ride rippled through his hair and his curving mustache.

He played *Wooden-leg Diana* and *Rocky Hollow Hard Times* and *My Mule, Aunt Nell* as the flat-boat skipped by Memphis and Helena and Greenville. He played *Hop Light Ladies* and *Leather Breeches* and *Dead up the Stump* while they were passing Vicksburg and Natchez and Baton Rouge. The moon had come up by that time and it was dodging in and out among the clouds while Jim played and he was enjoying it immensely.

Suddenly there was New Orleans in a big bend of the river and the flat-boat was making for shore. Out of the water on the dead run came the big bear, still hitched to the anchor-chain. There was an explosive noise and the biggest catfish ever seen in the Mississippi hit the bank with terrific force and flopped high into the air, landing fifty-seven feet out on the levee where it kept its tail slapping around for a month. The flat-boat ran full length up on the levee before the anchor-chain broke and the bear got away. Jim Higgins had beat the steamboat by a full day and a half because when his bear had jumped overboard with the anchor-chain tied to one leg that gigantic hungry catfish had chased him all the way to New Orleans.

Just to celebrate Jim's remarkable story, let's sing the song he was teaching the bear to dance to when Mr. Roosevelt's steamboat came along. Sing it as if you expected to see a mighty fancy steamboat come round the bend any minute.

[113]

THE BOATMAN DANCE

With a snappy swing

The boat-men dance, The boat-men sing, The
And when the boat - men come on shore, They

boat-men up to eve - ry thing
spend their money and work for more.

Chorus

Then dance the boat - man dance O

dance the boat - man dance, We

dance all night 'til broad day-light, Go home

with the girls in the morn-in'. O,

high row, the boat men row,

Float-in' down the riv-er, the O – hi – o.

The oyster boat should keep to shore,
The fishing smack should venture more;

The schooner sails before the wind,
The steamboat leaves a streak behind.

Joe Magerac

Joe Magerac

SOME PEOPLE SAY that Joe Magerac was born in a coal car and that when it was up-ended to let the coal rattle down, the breaker, Steve Mestrovic (who was a breaker-boy then, picking out bad pieces and throwing them away), saw him sliding by, lifted him out, and set him to work as his helper. Others claim Joe was born in an iron ore car and got run through the furnaces, melted, and refined into A-1 steel. Whichever it was, so far as anybody down in the Pennsylvania coal mines or steel mills knows, Joe is the only all-steel, coal-eyed man in those parts.

Nobody paid much attention to Joe at first. Until he was eighteen or so he lived in a slag pile and worked twenty-four hours a day. This gave him very little extra time to play baseball or duck-on-a-rock which is a very popular game among Pennsylvania small boys. By that time Steve Mestrovic had gone from the coal breaker to the steel mills in Pittsburgh and was known as the best steel puddler in the whole state. He had married a fine strong Hungarian girl and had a daughter, Josephine, who grew up to be the prettiest sixteen-year-old in the whole Monongahela Valley. In fact, she was so pretty that practically every unmarried steel-worker within a hundred miles of Pittsburgh had applied to Steve for a father's permission to marry her.

Steve finally was so pestered by all the boys who wanted to be Josephine's steady fellow and her intended husband, that he decided to hold a contest to decide who should be first choice. He advertised in all the Pittsburgh morning papers that on the third Saturday in November he would hold a big party in his house for all the strongest single men around and about—and the one who could lift the greatest weight would receive as a prize the blessing of Josephine's father as the favored beau of Josephine.

When the great Saturday came Steve's house was completely cut off from view by as husky a lot of giants as the Allegheny Mountains could produce. Steve's wife had to make a rule that only two of them at a time could bend over and come in for a piece of cake and a glass of sweet Tokay wine. (It was that kind of a party—very polite and refined.)

After everyone had had refreshments the lifting contest started. The first weights were steel bars that tipped the scales at five hundred pounds. They were too heavy for half of the fifty giants who tried to pick them up. Then the twenty-five who succeeded in lifting them tried lifting one in each hand, and a man from southern York State broke his left arm and had to go home. By that time there were only five strong fellows left, and three of those gave up after failing to lift three of the bars together in a bundle.

The two giants still in the contest were Tony, the son of Romeo Pacello who lived over in Northampton County, and Stanley Winawski whose Polish father worked in Scranton. Tony scorned the iron bars for his next try. A train of coal cars, rolling from one of the mines had stopped for a moment on the crossing outside Steve Mestrovic's home, and Tony went over and lifted the last car clean from the tracks. That gave Stanley an idea and he uncoupled the last two cars and held them both above his head. It looked as if Tony had won, and Josephine was just beginning to smile at him when Joe Magerac walked up and took off his shirt. Everybody gasped, for Joe's body was all one piece of shining tempered steel and his eyes burned like live black coals as he stepped up to the locomotive, picked it up, turned it around and set it down, faced toward the mine again. "Go pick up a clean coal car," said Joe to the engineer, "for Josephine and I are going on our honeymoon."

So Joe and Josephine were married and went to Niagara Falls on their honeymoon. And after they came back to the Monongahela Valley they lived very happily except for a quarrel once in a while. It was one of these quarrels which almost gave this story an unhappy ending. For Josephine was so annoyed with Joe for working twenty-four hours a day and having so little time left to spend at home, that one day when he dashed over to see her between shifts she said:

"This time you're not going back."

"I've got to," said Joe, "or I'll be late."

"Then take this with you," said Josephine, and she threw a pitcher full of water in his face.

No sooner had Josephine lost her temper than she regretted it, but she was sorry too late. For though Joe's body was tempered, rustless steel, his eyes really *were* burning coals and the water dashing against them blinded him and at the same time turned into clouds of steam.

Josephine was frantic, for she had put out her husband's eyes.

So Joe stayed home while she went down to the breakers and asked all the breaker-boys to look for especially bright, shiny-black coals that might be used instead of the eyes she had ruined. Soon two of the boys brought her exactly what she wanted, and she went back to Joe and replaced the old dull eyes with two lumps of coal that burned even brighter than the eyes he had owned before. Once more Joe and Josephine were happy.

But nowadays when the clouds hang low above the mines and look like rolling steam, the miners say to one another, "Joe and Josephine have been quarreling again." And when a breaker-boy seems to be working especially hard, his friends say, "He's looking for another pair of eyes for Joe Magerac." Then all the breaker-boys laugh together and sing the coal-miner's song, a song that their fathers and their grandfathers, too, have been singing for many years.

It's called *Down in a Coal-mine* and this is the way it goes.

I am a happy, happy boy, and glad as glad can be.
For if the days are good or bad it's all the same to me:
O little of the world I know, and care less for its ways,
For where the bright stars never glow, I wear away my days.

Chorus
    Down in a coal mine, underneath the ground,
    Where a gleam of sunshine never can be found;
    Digging dusky diamonds all the season round,
    Down in a coal mine, underneath the ground.

Then cheer up, boys, and make as much of every day you can,
But let your joy be always great as that of any man,
However we may dig and delve we'll still be happy souls.
What would our country be without the lads that look for coals?

DOWN IN A COAL MINE

Down in — the coal mine,

un - der-neath the ground, —

Where a gleam of sun - shine

nev - er can be found; —

Dig - ging dusk - y dia - monds

all __ the sea - son round, ___

Down in __ a coal mine,

un - der-neath the ground.

Annie Christmas

Annie Christmas

ANNIE CHRISTMAS WAS the strongest woman ever to pilot a flat-boat downriver from Cairo to New Orleans. She used to do her own loading and folks who lived at Natchez-under-the-Hill, which lies below the old city of Natchez, used to say that many a time they had seen her striding aboard with a barrel of flour balanced on top of her head and another under each arm. When she put all of her three-hundred-pound weight and her six-foot-eight height into leaning against the sweeps, her flatboat would begin skipping downriver at an amazing rate.

One of the stories river folk love to tell about Annie has to do with the time she and her crew were bushwhacking their empty flat upriver to Helena, Arkansas, for a load of turkeys, and a gang of outlaws who were camped in that big hole-in-the-ground known as Cave-in-Rock took them by surprise, bound them with iron chains, and carried them into the cave. There the leader of the outlaw band, angry because he had expected to find a rich cargo on the boat, told them that he was going to weight them down with rocks bound to their feet and throw them into the Mississippi to drown. That made Annie Christmas so angry that she began to swell up and her chains became tighter and tighter. Finally, with a fierce cracking noise they burst, flying about the cave and killing three men. Freed from her bonds, Annie Christmas bounded forward and, grabbing the cruel leader in her mighty right hand, heaved him toward the rock-ceiling of the cave. So great was the force of her throw that the unlucky wretch went right through the roof and was never heard from again. The hole that his body made through the top of the cave is still to be seen, however. It was a great convenience for some of the outlaws who later lived in the cave, for if they were pursued and surrounded by officers of the law they would use it as a secret passage for escape.

The most famous of all the deeds of Annie Christmas was her race upriver to Natchez, dragging her flat-boat behind her. Indeed, it was this unbelievable event which gave her her name, for up to the time it took place she had been known as "Annie," or sometimes as "Big Annie."

She and her crew had been eagerly waiting all of one early December for a whole boatload of toys which a clipper ship was bringing from Paris, France, for the Christmas joy of Natchez children. But the winter days went slowly by and there were no sails downriver. Christmas was near and the little girls of the old city beside the Mississippi would have no dainty French dolls, the little boys no barking, tail-wagging, woolly poodles on the morning of the birthday of Jesus.

At last, at noon on December twenty-fourth Annie Christmas and her crew saw the ballooning white sails of the storm-weary clipper above the levee and knew that the toys would soon be at the dock.

"Get ready to unload as soon as she throws out her gangplank," said Annie Christmas to her crew. "Put the toys in the flatboat and I'll take care of the rest."

As the plank came thundering down Annie's crew swarmed aboard. In two hours' time the flatboat was loaded to heaping fullness with the gay toys.

"Give me the towrope and cast her off," said Annie.

She put the rope over her shoulder and started upriver for Natchez. Slowly the flat-boat got under way. Annie leaned forward and tugged with all her strength. She began to walk slowly along the river path. Then her steps were faster and faster. She broke into a run and the flat-boat began to skip over the river's rippling waves, hardly touching the water. All that afternoon she ran. It was suppertime when she was passing the old town of Baton Rouge and the lights in the houses along the river seemed to threw out welcoming signals; but she did not stop. Night came and Annie galloped on through the starry darkness with the precious load of toys speeding swiftly on the gleaming water behind her.

It was the dawn of Christmas day and the first bells were ringing from the church towers when Annie raced into Natchez-under-the-Hill and tied up her boat. A great crowd of anxious fathers and mothers were awaiting her and soon the flat-boat was empty once more. But all over the old city on the bluff above the river, little boys and girls were waking to visions of clever, laughter-making French toys that turned out to be not visions at all but real. And that afternoon a singing arose from hundreds of happy Natchez homes, a singing from the mouths of hundreds of happy children—and they sang an old French song-of-happiness that they all knew. Annie, resting beside the great Mississippi at the docks of Natchez-under-the-Hill, heard it and was glad that she had run all night to bring the toys to the town. Ever afterwards she was known as Annie Christmas because of what she had done for the children of Natchez on that dark night-before-Christmas.

Sing the song-of-happiness now—as if the flat-boat loaded with toys had arrived this morning.

FAIS DO-DO

Very spirited

Fais   do - do,   Fais   do - do,

Fais   do - do,   dans les   bras   ton pa - pa

FAIS DO-DO

Fais do-do, fais do-do, fais do-do, dans les bras ton papa.
Fais do-do, fais do-do, fais do-do, dans les bras ton papa.

Fais do-do, fais-do-do, fais do-do, dans les bras ta mama.
Fais do-do, fais-do-do, fais do-do, dans les bras ta mama.

Fais do-do, fais do-do, fais do-do, dans les bras ta tante.
Fais do-do, fais do-do, fais do-do, dans les bras ta tante.

Bill Cropper

Bill Cropper

OLD BILL CROPPER WAS mate on the fanciest of all the fancy float-ing palaces that folks called steamboats where the Ohio River dips southwest along the Kentucky shore. Her name was the *Ranny Doddler* and she knew every navigable inch of river water in her neck of the woods. She was so pretty and so white that some folks called her the "birthday cake" boat and she was so fancy that others called her the "gingerbread queen." The band of decoration that took the wind between her two feathered and smoking stacks was so full of curlicues and of skew-gees that jealous rivermen used to say Bill Cropper had hung a strip of lace from the edge of his wife's petticoat up there.

The *Ranny Doddler* was fast, too. The people who lived along the banks of the Big Kanawha and the Licking whispered it around that Bill had set all the black deckhands to catching eels for a month. After they had a fearful mess of them he had dumped every last eel in the big black frying pan of the *Ranny Doddler's* galley and tried all the grease out of them. Then he sent each deckhand overboard to dive under and slap a handful of eel grease against the

Ranny Doddler's bottom. From then on she high-balled past the swiftest of the river packets and made them look tied to a stump.

The *Ranny Doddler* would float on anything even slightly moist. On a blowy day after she got the eel-grease treatment she would sometimes run three or four inches above the river surface—floating merrily along on the windy spray. Bill claimed after this had happened a few times that her draft was a minus four inches and out of sheer bravado he ran her over a ten-foot falls instead of going through the lock. She came down on the mist kicked up by the falls as easy as if she were sinking into a featherbed.

The *Ranny Doddler* got stuck only twice when Bill Cropper was mate on her. The first time was when she tried to ride out the big flood some years ago and the waters of the Licking went down so fast that the first thing anybody knew there was the *Ranny Doddler* high and dry in the top of a Kentucky elm. Bill had to wait all day up there until he could float her down on the evening dew.

The other time was when the *Ranny Doddler* steamed up the big Kanawha for a cargo of West Virginia turkeys. She made the upriver jaunt easily enough though the water was low in a dry season. But when she was coming back down, the water just plumb gave out and left the *Ranny Doddler* sitting on a sandbar.

Her captain tried hosing her out from the bank and he tried

walking her over on sticks, but she would not budge. Then up spoke old Bill Cropper.

"Cap'n," he said. "Let me try to git her off."

"What do you calc'late on doin'?" said the captain.

"Ef'n you'll have a boy bring that barrel of brads and that spool of steel cable up from below and a few crates o' turkeys as well, I'll show ye."

So the captain ordered the brads and cable and turkeys brought up to the hurricane deck.

"Cut that cable in fifty-foot lengths and nail one end of each length to the deck with a brad," said Bill.

The deckhands did as he directed.

"Now take those turkeys out of the crates and make each loose cable-end fast to a leg of a turkey."

The order was obeyed.

"I'm goin' to get my shotgun," said Bill, "and I'm goin' to fire it from the stern. About a half-second later we'll be on our way."

As the shotgun roared from the stern the turkeys rose from the deck in whirring fright. A moment later they had settled into harness and the *Ranny Doddler* was sliding up into the air. In a minute there was deep water below her.

"Throw some corn on the deck," said Bill, and a deckhand scattered the yellow kernels. The turkeys recovered from their fright and settled back to the deck, contentedly pecking at the corn.

"Put 'em back in their crates," said Bill. "We're floatin' free and tonight I'll be dancin' *Way Down in the Paw-Paw Patch* with my wife, at one of the rip-roarin'est play-parties ever held in these parts."

We might as well join Bill and his wife at the party, for really doing a good job of dancing and singing *Way Down in the Paw-Paw Patch* requires quite a few people. Here goes.

BOYS FORM A LINE *facing* a line of girls. As the song starts the first girl (Betty) runs around the whole group coming back to her place at the end of the last line of the first stanza. At the second verse the first boy leads his line in a circle around the girls (the girls stand clapping hands) and back to their original places. Then singing the third verse the first boy and first girl lead around their own line, the others following. As the leaders meet at the end of the line they raise their arms above their heads, hands clasped, and let the other couples pass beneath (leaving first couple at end of line). Repeat song from the beginning changing the name of girl to that of next in line and so on until all have formed the ladder.

WAY DOWN IN THE PAW-PAW PATCH

Tony Beaver

Tony Beaver

TONY BEAVER IS either the greatest lumberjack in the world or the next thing to it. If you live in a Northern state like Maine or Wisconsin, Michigan or Oregon you probably think Paul Bunyan is the greatest lumberjack and that his cousin Tony runs him a poor second. But if you live down in the middle South where the Big Smoky Mountains lift pine-covered slopes toward softer skies you are likely to think Tony Beaver is worth a whole raft of Paul Bunyans.

Down in the Big Smoky Mountains the Eel River twists and turns about so much that sometimes it runs into itself and dashes round and round in a perfect circle. When that happens the lumberjacks who live at Tony Beaver's camp beside the river and ride the logs to the sawmill begin to get dizzy from circling so fast. They might as well be on a merry-go-round. After they have passed Tony's camp ten or eleven times and their brains are whirling as much as the river, they usually guess what has happened. Another way they can tell that the river is running into itself is that all at once the water is full of gilli-galoo fish who live only in perfectly round rivers and lakes. Before anybody can say "Jack Robinson" there is such a grist of gilli-galoos in the river that there is no room for lumber and the logs wing-up on the banks. When the lumber-jacks see this happening they call for Tony Beaver to come and help them and Tony comes striding across the tops of the Big Smoky Mountains and says in a big voice:

"What have you whistle-punks and road-monkeys done now?"

Then Tony's lumberjacks say, "Tony, this isn't winter time, it's spring. When the snow was on the ground we loaded up the big sleds with logs and the whistle-punks saw to it they were hitched together right, and the road-monkeys spread sand on the steepest slopes so that the sleds wouldn't get going too fast and run into each other, and we brought the logs down the mountains and dumped them on the ice of the river. Then the thaw came and the ice went out and the snow melted into the river and made it rise up over its banks and run so fast it turned white with foam. So now we're whitewater men, Tony, and nobody works in the foam better than we do. There isn't any use of working, though, when the Eel River has run into itself and is going round and round and the gilli-galoo fish have crowded the logs out on the banks."

So then Tony turns to the camp cook and says:

"Cookie, mix up a big mess of pancake batter and bring it down here in your kettle."

And when cookie has brought the pancake batter in his big kettle to the bank, Tony says:

"Dump it in."

No sooner has the pancake batter hit the water than it sticks to the rocks and the baking powder in it begins to work and the batter begins to rise. Soon it has risen so high it has formed a solid dam against which the white water splashes in vain. Higher and higher the water rises but higher and higher lifts the batter and the water cannot flow over the top. At last the water has risen so high that it has overflowed the banks and it pours down the mountains in a new course to the Levels far below, where the flat land lies close to the sea. At once the gilli-galoos disappear, for they cannot live in a river if it is no longer round. Then Tony picks up the sawmill that stands beside the old course of the water and sets it down beside the new river-bed. At once the logs begin floating down to it and the saws begin to whine through them, making them into many boards. The lumberjacks are happy once more, and as they ride the logs down the Eel River that dashes down the sides of the southern mountains, they sing a song about one of their highest neighbors, a mountain called *Old Smoky*.

OLD SMOKIE

OLD SMOKIE

It's raining, it's hailing,
  The stars give no light.
My horses can't travel
  This dark stormy night.

Go put them in the stable
  And give them some hay,
Come sit in my cabin
  As long as you stay.

My horses aren't hungry
  They won't eat your hay,
And I must be riding
  Until it is day.

I'll go to Old Smokie,
  The mountain so high,
I'll meet all my friends in
  The land of the sky.

Daniel Boone

Daniel Boone

SOME AMERICAN HEROES have been great Indian fighters and some have been great bear fighters, but it took a pretty smart man to be both. Being a bear fighter was very different from being an Indian fighter. For instance, it is not at all difficult to get a good hold on a bear, but it is very hard to get any kind of a hold on a slippery Indian. As a rule, the hold that a hunter got on a bear had to be a good one, for once he had it he dared not let go. As for fighting Indians, you just could not make any rules at all.

Of all the combination bear-and-Indian fighters produced in the early days of our country, Daniel Boone was thought by most people to be the smartest. Here are a couple of reasons why they thought so.

The first is a bear story that did not really begin as a bear story. According to the folks who tell it, Daniel Boone had been in the woods for many weeks when he came upon a stretch that seemed quite unfamiliar to him and made him a little uncertain as to where he was. I say "a little uncertain" because when he was an old man Daniel said that in all his life he had never been lost in the woods though one time he had been kind of "bewildered" for about three days.

So to get rid of his uncertainty Daniel climbed a tall tree and looked about him until he was satisfied where he was—right down to a T. Then he started to come down. He had almost reached the main crotch of the tree when a rotten limb gave way beneath his moccasined foot and he fell. There was a hole just at the main crotch and Daniel fell plumb into it.

He was not hurt, but he was annoyed when he found out what had happened to him. The trunk of the tree was hollow and he had landed on the inside at the bottom. The sides were so smooth he could not climb them and so high he could not reach up and pull himself out. He was a prisoner with no way of escape.

All the rest of the day he stood there looking up through the hole at the top to the blue sky and the free-drifting white clouds. Night came and he began to wonder if he would ever get out. Perhaps he would have to stay there and starve to death.

About an hour after complete darkness had come, Daniel heard a strange noise. There was a scratching and a grunting on the outside of his prison. Some sort of animal was climbing the tree, for the noise was getting higher and higher. Suddenly he knew that the hole above him was filled up, for he could no longer see the star that had been shining down on him. Then the scratching and grunting started again but this time it was coming down toward him. Daniel could tell from the fact that the scratching was nearer to him than the grunts that the animal was coming down backwards, and instantly he realized that he had fallen into the hollow-tree home of a big bear.

Slowly the bear backed down toward him. Foot by foot the distance between Daniel and the hindquarters of the fierce beast grew less. All of a sudden Daniel jumped upward and grabbed the bear by his stubby tail. "Aiooup!" he yelled at the top of his voice.

The bear was so frightened at this unexpected attack that he gave one big grunt and dashed up out of the hole just about a hundred times as fast as he had come down into it. Daniel kept his hold on the tail and went along with him. Down the trunk went the bear and off into the woods. Daniel turned a complete somersault when he finally let go.

Well, that is how Daniel Boone outsmarted a bear. He was just as good at outsmarting Indians. The story that most people like to tell to prove it starts at the point where Daniel discovered that he was being followed by a war-party of redskins. The savages did not realize that Daniel knew they were behind him. They flitted noiselessly from tree to tree, closing in gradually, waiting until they could all jump on Daniel at once. But Daniel could always tell when there were Indians about. He quickened his pace until the Indians found it hard to keep up with him. Indeed it seemed that he was about to slip away from them completely when suddenly he came out on a high bluff above a narrow river. Now he was in greater danger than ever. If he dove into the water the

Indians could easily shoot him as he swam for the other bank. They were getting closer and closer. Daniel looked about him for some way of escape. From a tall sycamore that grew on the bluff hung long streamers of wild grapevines. They were tough and strong. He grabbed them and tried his weight on them. They held him firmly. Holding the longest ones in his grasp he turned and ran toward the Indians behind him. When he had almost reached them he whirled about and ran as fast as he could. He reached the edge of the bluff and leaped out over the river with all the strength in his legs. The vines swung him at a dizzy height over the swirling water below. On and on he went. The Indians had reached the bluff and stood there shouting their surprise. He could see that he was nearing the far bank. Suddenly he was there and hurling himself forward into the shadow of the woods. He was safe. No Indian of the pursuing party dared use the grapevine swing and Daniel went on unmolested.

Now let's sing a song that was made up especially for Daniel Boone because he came upon the great meadowlands of Kentucky through the ravine of the Cumberland River. It is called *Cumberland Gap* and you will sing it better if you remember while you sing that Daniel was smarter than any bear or any Indian in the wilderness.

CUMBERLAND GAP

CUMBERLAND GAP

Cumberland Gap is a noted place,
Cumberland Gap is a noted place,
Cumberland Gap is a noted place;
Three kinds of water for to wash your face.

Cumberland Gap with its cliff and rocks,
Cumberland Gap with its cliff and rocks,
Cumberland Gap with its cliff and rocks;
Home of the panther, and the bear and fox.

Daniel Boone stood on Pinnacle Rock,
Daniel Boone stood on Pinnacle Rock,
Daniel Boone stood on Pinnacle Rock;
He killed Indians with an old flintlock.

Lie down, boys, and take a little nap,
Lie down, boys, and take a little nap,
Lie down, boys, and take a little nap;
Fourteen miles to the Cumberland Gap.

De Knee-High Man

De Knee-High Man

DE KNEE-HIGH MAN lived by de swamp. He wuz alwez a-wantin' to be big 'stead of little. He sez to hisself: "I is gwinter ax de biggest thing in dis neighborhood how I kin git sizable." So he goes to see Mr. Horse. He ax him: "Mr. Horse, I come to git you to tell me how to git big like you is."

Mr. Horse, he say: "You eat a whole lot of corn and den you run round and round and round, till you ben about twenty miles and atter a while you big as me."

So de knee-high man, he done all Mr. Horse tole him. An' de corn make his stomach hurt, and runnin' make his legs hurt and de trying make his mind hurt. And he gits littler and littler. Den de knee-high man he set in his house and study how come Mr. Horse ain't help him none. And he say to hisself: "I is gwinter go see Brer Bull."

So he go to see Brer Bull and he say: "Brer Bull, I come to ax you to tell me how to git big like you is."

And Brer Bull, he say: "You eat a whole lot o' grass and den

[158]

you bellow and bellow and fust thing you know you gits big like I is."

And de knee-high man he done all Brer Bull tole him. And de grass make his stomach hurt, and de bellowing make his neck hurt and de thinking make his mind hurt. And he git littler and littler. Den de knee-high man he set in his house and he study how come Brer Bull ain't done him no good. Atter while, he hear ole Mr. Hoot Owl way in de swamp preachin' dat de bad peoples is sure gwinter have de bad luck.

Den de knee-high man he say to himself: "I gwinter ax Mr. Hoot Owl how I kin git to be sizable," and he go to see Mr. Hoot Owl.

And Mr. Hoot Owl say: "What for you want to be big?" and de knee-high man say: "I wants to be big so when I gits in a fight, I ken whup."

And Mr. Hoot Owl say: "Anybody ever try to pick a scrap wid you?"

De knee-high man he say naw. And Mr. Hoot Owl say: "Well den, you ain't got no cause to fight, and you ain't got no cause to be mo' sizable 'an you is."

De knee-high man say: "But I wants to be big so I can kin see a fur ways." Mr. Hoot Owl, he say: "Can't you climb a tree and see a fur ways when you is clim' to de top? And ain't you see de seven stars of de Drinkin' Gourd and don't dey tell you where to go?"

De knee-high man, he say: "Yes." Den Mr. Hoot Owl say: "You ain't got no cause to be bigger in de body, but you sho' is got cause to be bigger in de BRAIN."

Den Mr. Hoot Owl hoot three times and shut his mouth for good an' hit got dark in de woods. De knee-high man was scared as he could be becuz he don' know the way back home. At fust he began to cry an' he say, "I'm lost in de woods an' nobody'll ever fin' me till I'm starved to death an' lookin' mighty peaked an' even smaller than I is now. But den he 'membered what Mr. Hoot Owl say about if he clim' a tall tree he could see de seven stars of de Drinkin' Gourd.

So de knee-high man he pick him out a tall lolly pine tree an' he clim' an' he clim' till he come to de top. An' dere sho' nuff high up in de sky de seven stars of de Drinkin' Gourd was pintin' him de way to go home.

Den he slid down de tree an' he walk back to his home in de swamp all de time singin' out loud so he kin git over bein' scared.

Now all you chillen jest pertend you is walkin' back home in de black woods an' sing real loud to keep from bein' scared out of what wits you got. Sing de song about de Drinkin' Gourd dat tells folks how to go home in de dark.

FOLLOW THE DRINKING GOURD

Slowly and deliberately

When the sun comes back, When the first quail calls, Then the time has come Fol - low the drink - ing gourd.

Chorus

Fol - low the drink - ing gourd,

Fol - low the drink - ing gourd; For the

old man says,

"Fol - low the drink - ing gourd."

Where the river ends,   Where the great big lake,
Just between two hills,   Flows into the stream,
Go on to the right,   There the old man waits,
Follow the drinking gourd.   Follow the drinking gourd.

Brer Rabbit and Sis Cow

Brer Rabbit and Sis Cow

BRER RABBIT he don' get out-smarted more'n once or twice't since de year de stars fell. Brer Rabbit he know how smart he be but sometimes he gits fooled just like most everybody.

One of dose times was when Brer Rabbit meet Mr. Tony Beaver comin' from his grandma's an' totin' a bundle of fresh-made buck-wheat cakes de ol' lady give him.

Brer Rabbit say:

"Hit shore is mighty nice runnin' slap into you, Mr. Tony Beaver, jis' at dis time. I see you're totin' of a few of your grandma's buckwheat cakes. Now I got persimmons in dis here pail and I knows how to fix it so's you an' me kin have twicet as many. You jes lay a pancake down on dat log and I'll lay a persimmon beside it. Den do de same agin till we runs out of pancakes an' persimmons. When dey's all laid out I'll say some conjure words an' dey'll be twiced as many as dey was before."

So Tony Beaver he lays out a pancake an' Brer Rabbit he lays a persimmon beside it an says:

"First a persimmon an' den a cake.

Don't let me ketch no belly-ache."

[166]

Den when de pancakes all give out Brer Rabbit he say, "Bingo!" an' grab all de cakes an' persimmons an' start to run off wid dem.

But Mr. Tony Beaver he was too quick for Brer Rabbit an' he rare back an' fetch him a kick dat knock him high as a spring kite. De wind catched in his big ears an' sent him sailin' all round de sky an' all de time he drop pancakes an' persimmons. All de little chillen run out wid gunny sacks an' baskets an' pick up pancakes an' persimmons fer days on end. Folks round here still talkin' 'bout de time hit rained pancakes an' persimmons out of a clear sky.

Brer Rabbit was a lot smarter de time he meet up wid Sis Cow.

Brer Rabbit see Sis Cow an' she have a bag plumb full of milk, an' it's a hot day an' he ain't had nothin' to drink fur a long time. He know 't ain't no use askin' her fur milk 'cause las' year she done 'fused him onct, and when his ole 'oman was sick, too.

Brer Rabbit begun thinkin' mighty hard. Sis Cow is grazin' under a persimmon tree, an' de persimmons is turned yellow, but they ain't ripe enough yit to fall down.

So Brer Rabbit, he say: "Good mornin', Sis Cow."

"Good mornin', Brer Rabbit."

"How is you feelin' dis mornin', Sis Cow?"

"Poly, Brer Rabbit, I'se jest sorter haltin' twix a balk and a breakdown, Brer Rabbit."

Brer Rabbit express his sympathy and then he say: "Sis Cow,

would you do me the favor to hit this here persimmon tree with yore head an' shake down a few of dem persimmons?"

Sis Cow say, "Sure," an' she hits the tree, but no persimmons come down. They ain't ripe enough yit.

So den Sis Cow git mad an' she go to the top of de hill an' she hists her tail over over her back and here she come a bilin'. She hit dat tree *so* hard dat her horns go right into the wood so fur she can't pull 'em out.

"Brer Rabbit," says Sis Cow, "I implores you to help me git a-loose." But Brer Rabbit say: "No, Sis Cow, I can't git you a-loose. I'm a mighty weakly man, Sis Cow. But I kin empty your bag, Sis Cow, and I'm goin' to do it fur you."

Then Brer Rabbit he go home for his ole 'oman and de chillun an' dey come back to de persimmon tree an' milk Sis Cow and have a big feastin'. When they were all full up to their ears de whole

family had a big romp through de cotton patch while de boll weevils, dey look up from stuffin' of demselves on de cotton an' den go back to work. Pretty soon all de rabbit family git shore wore out an' dey sits in a row in de cotton patch an' sing a song about de boll weevil.

Jes' stan' in de same row wid 'em an' sing, too.

THE BOLL WEEVIL

Moderately fast

The Boll Wee-vil's a lit-tle bug From

Mex - i - co, they say, And he

came up to try the Tex-as soil And

thought he bet - ter stay,

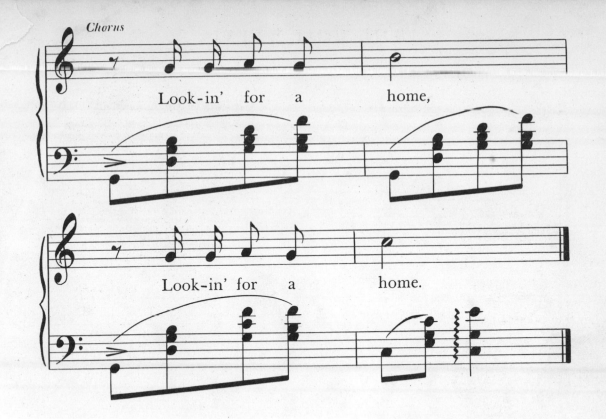

Look-in' for a home,

Look-in' for a home.

The first I saw the Boll Weevil
He's sitting on the square,
And the next time I saw the Boll Weevil
He had his family there—
Lookin' for a home,
Lookin' for a home.

The Farmer took the Boll Weevil
And buried him in sand;
And the Boll Weevil said to the Farmer,
"I'll stand it like a man,
For it is my home,
For it is my home."

Boll Weevil said to the Farmer,
"Just leave me here alone,
For I've eat'n up all your cotton crop
Now I'll begin on corn,
For I'll have a home,
For I'll have a home."

John Henry

John Henry

JOHN HENRY WAS the greatest steel-driving black boy of all time.
Folks used to come from miles around to see him whop steel spikes
down into solid rock. He started out whopping steel with a nine-
pound hammer but he wound up with a twelve-pound hammer.
Some say he whopped down every spike in the whole Central of
Georgia Railroad. Every time the great head of his hammer hit
the head of a steel spike he'd grunt and the head of the spike would
be six inches lower than it was before. Then his shaker, the black
boy who held the spike steady for him, would shake the spike a
little so that it would be free to move on down and John Henry
would raise his hammer again. If there was a good singer singing,
John Henry and the shaker would fall in with the rhythm of his
song and beat it out. Hammer falling—unh!—shaker shaking—
hammer rising—hammer falling once more—unh!

John Henry died long ago and this story finally gets around
to telling about it. Some folks say, though, that he did not really
die. When on clear summer evenings, there come from the wooded
slopes of the southern mountains, sharp sounds of steel meeting
steel they say that John Henry has come back and is whopping
steel again. They say:

John Henry's back in the mountains
Can't you hear that hammer rain?
He's hung it in that big blue hill
He's a-drivin' steel again.

And every time that hammer hits
You can hear his shaker shout.
And every time that hammer hits
A thousand stars fly out.

John Henry's building railroad
Layin' track for a million cars;
John Henry's back in the mountains
He's whoppin' out the stars.

But this is the story that started all the fuss about John Henry, the story of how he came to die.

One day when the Central of Georgia was building, a slick Yankee stranger came to see the white bossman.

"Cap'n," he said, "want to buy a newfangled, nickelplated, doublejointed steam drill that's worth all the black boy whoppers from here to New Orleans?"

"No," said the bossman, "there's a black boy whopping for me who can send the steel down faster and deeper than all your fancy metal steam hammers."

"Couldn't be," said the Yankee. "No black boy can whop it

down as fast as my steam whopper. Show me one that can and I'll give you my machine."

And so a contest was arranged between the big black man and the shiny drill. People came from Georgia and Mississippi and Alabama to see it. John Henry's wife, Lucy, put on her best red dress and she took her little baby in her arms, and she set out proudly for the place where the contest was to be. When she got there the machine was already hissing and clanking while the fire deep within it glowed red. John Henry stood straight, holding his twelve-pound hammer; "I'm a steel-drivin' man," he said.

Soon came the signal to begin and the drill puffed and jangled and its hammer began to beat. Although it got in two good licks before John Henry started, they didn't count for much when his twelve-pound hammer hit the head of the steel spike held by his shaker.

"Wow!" said the shaker, twisting the spike about and settling it for the next blow. Already eight inches of its length were out of sight in the hard rock.

But the Yankee stranger pulled a lever somewhere on the machine and it began to run faster, hammering the steel down with more strokes a minute than any black whopper could give it.

"Give me another twelve-pound hammer," said John Henry. "I'll use one in each hand. Just keep shakin' that steel, shaker boy."

The muscles of the big man stood out like strong thick ropes as he swung the two hammers. Clank, clank, clank they struck upon the long spikes and every time they struck, eight inches of steel bored deep into the rock. Rivers of sweat poured down John Henry's forehead. His shoulders were wet and shining. The machine was throbbing madly and its hammer was striking swiftly again and again. John Henry put on an extra effort and moved forward. His hammers swung easily in steady quick beats. Bit by bit he moved ahead of the machine. Slowly, very slowly, he left the steam drill behind.

Suddenly there was the shrill screech of a whistle. The battle between the man and the machine was over. John Henry raised both hammers high in the air, a look of joy on his face. Then he fell to the ground.

"I done beat it, but I'm dyin'," said John Henry.

Lucy rushed forward and took his big black head in her lap. On the red dress appeared a wide circle dark with sweat.

"Give me a cool drink of water before I die," said John Henry.

Lucy gave him a cool drink of water and then placed the little black baby in the palm of John Henry's left hand. John Henry looked down at his son. "Boy," he said, "you're goin' to be a steel-drivin' man."

With his right hand John Henry lifted his hammer. Hand and hammer dropped to his side. John Henry died with his hammer in his hand. After he died his friends made up a song about him.

Since we are his friends, too, let's join in.

JOHN HENRY

whop, let it whop that steel on down. Let it

whop, let it whop that steel on down."

John Henry told his captain
That a man he ain't nothin' but a man
"And before I'd let your steam drill beat me down
I would die with my hammer in my hand.
I would die with my hammer in my hand."

John Henry told his shaker
"O, my shaker, O, why don't you sing?
For I'm throwing twelve pound from my hips on down
Just you hear, just you hear that cold steel ring.
Just you hear, just your hear that cold steel ring."

John Henry walked the railroad,
With his big hammer hanging by his side.
He walked down the track, but he didn't come on back,
'Cause he laid down his hammer and he died.
'Cause he laid down his hammer and he died.

Spadebeard

Spadebeard

OF ALL THE VILLAINOUS PIRATES that used to lie in wait for unarmed vessels along our southern Atlantic coast, the giant Spadebeard was the worst—and the ugliest. The thick black hair that framed his swarthy face glowed with strange light; his pointed beard shone like an ebony spade; and his eyes glittered weirdly from their deep hollows.

The captains and the crews of ships that sailed along the shores of Virginia and the Carolinas feared Spadebeard because they knew he was without mercy. Whenever he took a vessel he made his helpless captives walk the plank and he laughed as, with hands tied behind their backs, they were forced off the long board's end to drop and drown and lie forever in Davy Jones's locker, which is the sailors' name for the bottom of the sea.

Among the people who like to sing the song that comes next in this book are many who live among the coves and islands where Spadebeard used to lurk when he was looking for more ships to rob and more innocent people to destroy. Some of them say that the song tells the story of what happened to Spadebeard and some of them even claim that the brave cabin boy who sank the pirate's ship was one of their ancestors.

Scholars tell them that the song is much older than they think and that the story it tells happened far across the ocean, but the singers just point out the lowlands near which, they say, the cabin boy sank the ship and repeat that they ought to know about it for he was a relative of theirs.

Then they go on and tell how after the ship was sunk and Spadebeard and all his terrible pirate crew were drowned, a great tidal wave came and swept the vessel up out of Davy Jones's locker and carried it on a foaming crest far inland, until it reached the Great Dismal Swamp. There it set her down, and there on nights of fierce lightning and growling thunder some people say she can still be seen. Swamp moss has covered her sails, they say, and her mast and spars are green with mould, but her crew still stands at her rusty guns waiting orders from Spadebeard standing high on her bridge. As he lifts an arm and lets it fall his men pull the lanyards and from the cannons' mouths silently flash streaks of green fire. For a moment the murky waters of the Great Dismal Swamp gleam with unearthly light and show the narrow bayous, like endless little winding rivers stretching into the mysterious distance. Then with the suddenness of a single thunderclap, the ship is swallowed up in blackness. Every once in a while on a stormy night, someone who lives beside the dank wooded edges of the Great Dismal Swamp says he has seen Spadebeard's ship. Then he and his neighbors shake their heads and say the pirate is getting just what he had coming to him. He is being punished for all his crimes, they say, for he is condemned forever to sail the awful waters of the Great Dismal Swamp in search of a cargo ship that he can never capture. And after they have said these things, then people remember the brave cabin boy and they all sing together the story of his brave deed.

Try to imagine yourselves in a little cabin on the sandy dunes of the Carolina coast when you sing this ballad called *Lowlands Low*.

LOWLANDS LOW

The captain sailed a ship, boys, and she put out to sea.
She went by the name of the Golden Willow Tree.
Said he, "I am afraid of the enemy I see,
As she sails upon the Lowlands, Lowlands,
As she sails upon the Lowlands Low."

But up then spoke our Jack, he was the cabin boy.
Said he, "What will you give me if them I will destroy?"
"O gold and silver store and my daughter dear for you,
If you sink them in the Lowlands, Lowlands,
If you sink them in the Lowlands Low."

Then Jack he took his auger, and jumped into the sea,
And swam along the side of the wicked enemy.
He put out all her lights and he let the water in,
And he sank her in the Lowlands, Lowlands,
And he sank her in the Lowlands Low.

Then Jack he turned around, swam around his good ship's side.
"O messmates take me in, I am going with the tide."
His captain took him in, and on the deck he died,
And they sank him in the Lowlands, Lowlands,
And they sank him in the Lowlands Low.

LOWLANDS LOW

In a slow, swinging rhythm

The cap — tain sailed a ship, boys, and she put out to sea. ___ She went by the name of the Gold — en Wil - low Tree. ___ Said he, – "I am a

fraid of the en - e my —— I -

see, As she sails u-pon the Low - lands,

Low — lands, As she sails u-pon the

Low — lands, Low."————

The Virginia Giant

The Virginia Giant

ONE DAY, LONG AGO, a young man on horseback trotted down a road in Virginia. The plume on his blue hat waved in the soft summer breeze and the silver buckles on his shoes flashed in the morning sun. As he rounded a bend he saw in the road ahead of him a wagon loaded with tobacco, stuck fast in a muddy hollow. He saw the six fine horses hitched to the wagon pull and strain, pull and strain, while the driver helped by pushing, but the wagon did not budge. Just as the driver sat down on the side of the road, tired and dejected, the young man pulled up his horse and jumped off.

"Good day, sir," he said. "You seem to be in trouble."

"Yes," answered the driver, sadly. "I've been stuck for hours. My horses can't move my wagon and I will lose my whole crop of tobacco."

"Your horses are tired," said the young man kindly. "Unhitch them and I will get your wagon out of the mud."

The driver was surprised by this strange request but he did as he was told. Then the stranger walked to a spot just behind the wagon. He put his shoulder against the back of it and pushed. The wagon creaked, and moved. Again he pushed and the front wheels rolled forward and upward until they rested on solid ground. Once more heave of his mighty shoulders and the wagon with its heavy load was safely out of the mud. The driver stood amazed and silent while the young man wiped the mud from his cherished silver buckles, mounted his horse and rode away.

Peter Francisco was only fifteen years old then, and he was six feet six inches tall in his stocking feet. He was already the biggest and the strongest man in the whole state and people were already beginning to call him The Virginia Giant.

On another day when Peter Francisco was riding his horse through the meadows, he came upon a crowd of farmers. They stood helplessly about, looking at a cow and her calf who had wandered from the meadow and had sunk so far into the swamp at the edge of it that they could not get out.

"Fetch some planks, please," said Peter. The farmers brought rails from a nearby fence and Peter told them to place them end to end on the marshy land until they made a path to the cow and her calf. This done, Peter walked to the end of the wooden path. First he put his strong right arm around the cow and slowly lifted her out of the mud. Next, with his left arm, he pulled up the calf. Then slinging the cow over his great shoulders and carrying the little calf under his arm, he walked out of the swamp to safety.

Peter fought for General Washington in the war of the American colonies for their independence. Some said he was so strong and fierce he could scare a whole British army into running away. After General Washington had heard of some of his brave deeds he had a special sword forged for him. It was a splendid and terrible weapon, with a broad steel blade five feet long and as sharp as a razor. Peter used it so well that he became a very famous warrior. The enemy were so afraid of him that they offered a large sum of money for his capture, dead or alive.

One day Peter sat in Ben Wand's tavern in Virginia, recovering from a wound. Suddenly he heard steps outside and before he could reach his sword, the door burst open. Eight red-coated English soldiers rushed in and surrounded Peter, sticking their eight sabers close to his ribs. Peter smiled and quietly surrendered. He was marched outside and searched. The officer in command said to him, "I will trouble you for the fine silver buckles on your shoes."

"Then take them off yourself," roared Peter.

As the officer stooped down to rob him of his dearest possession, Peter lifted his foot and sent the officer tumbling on the ground. Quickly he grabbed the famous sword which he had left standing by the door. Whacking the officer with the sword and yelling at the top of his lungs, Peter ran for a horse. The English soldiers, surprised and badly frightened by the angry young giant, scattered in all directions looking for a place to hide. Swinging the shining blade above his head and springing on the strongest horse, the Virginia Giant rode away. And as he rode he triumphantly sang a song that his fellow soldiers in the Revolution loved to sing as they marched, *Hi Betty Martin*.

When he reached his home he was so happy that he and his little sister danced to the tra-la-las just as you are about to do now.

HIGH, BETTY MARTIN

Trippingly

High, Bet-ty Mar-tin Tip toe tip toe,

High, Bet-ty Mar-tin Tip, toe, fine.

Dance and Sing
Tra la la la la la la la Tra la la la la la la la

Tra la la la la la la la Tip, toe, fine.

sfz

HIGH, BETTY MARTIN

"High, Betty Martin
Tip toe, tip toe,
High, Betty Martin
Tip, toe, fine."

Dance and Sing

Tra-la-la-la-la-la-la-la
Tra-la-la-la-la-la-la-la
Tra-la-la-la-la-la-la-la
Tip, toe, fine.

"Never found a man
To suit her fancy
Never found a man
To suit her mind."

Dance and Sing

Tra-la-la-la-la-la-la-la
Tra-la-la-la-la-la-la-la
Tra-la-la-la-la-la-la-la
Tip, toe, fine.

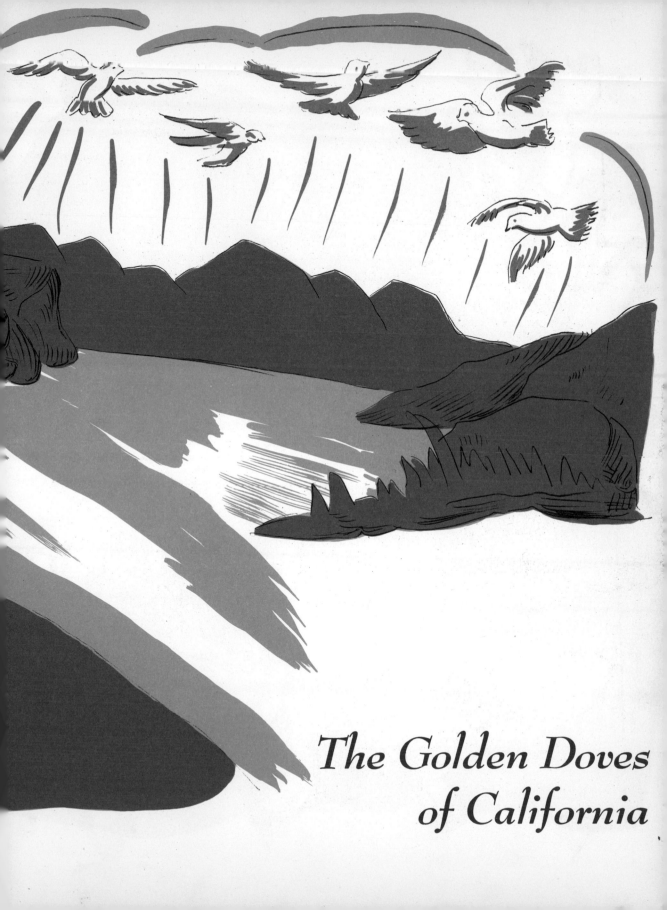

The Golden Doves
of California

The Golden Doves of California

IN THE DAYS BEFORE Captain Luis Arguello became Don Luis the Just, first Mexican governor of sunny California, he led a little group of Spanish explorers inland from the coast and north along the Sacramento River. Soon they had passed the clear waters of the stream we now call the American River and their path grew difficult for they were moving into country never seen before by white men.

One night, weary and aching from their travel, they camped by a rippling stream which they knew must roll downward from the high peaks to the eastward. And as they were deep in sleep they were awakened by strange, beautiful music in the sky and they saw above them a flock of bright golden doves spreading light through the darkness. All the rest of the night the Spaniards lay awake watching the splendid birds wheel in gleaming circles above them. But when the first gray of morning sifted down the eastern slopes the doves flew away toward the tall peaks above them. And when daylight had come, Captain Luis Arguello saw that the rolling current of the river was covered with a carpet of golden feathers. He called his men and they all ran down to the water and filled their hands with downy gold.

But when the feathers were drying in the heat of the sun they gradually became splotched with white, then white all over. None of them kept their gleaming gold, once they had been caught up in human hands.

"We shall call this stream 'El Rio de las Plumas,'" said Captain Luis Arguello, and to this day it is known by the English words of the same meaning—Feather River.

Many years later, when the great American showman, Phineas T. Barnum, inventor of the modern circus, had built his big museum in New York down by the waters of New York Harbor, he went into partnership with "Old Grizzly Adams" a California bear-tamer who told him many interesting tales of the wild animals of his native state. He spoke of a California leopard, a California hippopotamus, and even a California elephant he had once seen at a great distance, though it was very shy.

One day a strange-looking man who spoke with an accent so foreign that his words were not easily understood, presented himself to Mr. Barnum and Old Grizzly Adams. On his arm he carried a covered basket from which came sweet, low notes of music. When he took off the cover the two Americans saw cuddled in the basket a pair of doves whose feathers were shining gold. "The golden doves of California!" said Old Grizzly—for he knew the Feather River and had heard the story of Don Luis and his men.

"What will you give me for them?" said the man with the basket.

"Their weight in silver," said Mr. Barnum.

Scales were brought, the doves were weighed, and Mr. Barnum gave the stranger a bag of silver.

After the stranger had gone away, Mr. Barnum and Old Grizzly made a beautiful cage and they put the doves in it and set it in the place of honor in the museum. Above it they placed a sign which read "The Golden Doves of California," and many people came to see the lovely, shining birds.

But they had been in their cage only a few days when their wings were seen to be spotted with white. Before very long the birds were entirely white and they looked just like any of the white doves in the parks of New York. Mr. Barnum was very angry because he thought the stranger had painted the birds before selling them. But Old Grizzly Adams knew why they were no longer golden. He knew that Mr. Barnum was finding, just as Don Luis Arguello had found long ago, that the feathers of the Golden Doves of California will not stay bright and shining if they are held captive by human hands.

Just as wild things seem precious when they are wild and are not valued when they are tamed and spiritless—so wild, far places seem beautiful when they have not been travelled and become commonplace when we walk them every day. Even before the days of Don Luis Arguello the Spanish settlers of the new world of America sang a song about doves which told these truths.

Let us sing it now, pretending that we are looking on the green shores of sunny California for the first time.

FOUR LITTLE WHITE DOVES

In a waltz tempo

There were four lit - tle white doves, ___
Oh, the four lit - tle white doves, ___

Perched on a gab - le at home, ___
Were fly - ing in - to the west, ___

And they say to each oth - er, ___
And they say to each oth - er, ___

The far places call us to roam.
The new home is

al - ways the best.

Refrain

Oh, new fields look al-ways the fair-est,_____ From

un -der a broad som - bre-ro. _____

Wild Bill Corlett

Wild Bill Corlett

AMONG THE THOUSANDS of Americans who lit out for California when they heard the news of the discovery of gold along the banks of the Sacramento was Wild Bill Corlett. Bill was a young man then and about as powerful, his friends said, as they come. And what's more, they used to add, he was just as handy at doing useful things in water as he was on land. Wherever this young giant came from, and there seems to have been some disagreement as to that, there could not have been any doubt that his bringing up had a good deal of water in it.

It was natural, therefore, that after Bill had found a gold-bearing rock or two on the banks of the Sacramento, he sold them for enough money to buy a steamboat captain's outfit and earned his way from then on by picking up passengers instead of nuggets.

Bill's first command was the *Goodman Castle*, a floating palace so heavy with fancy dew-dads above the waterline, that to keep her from being tippy her builders gave her a deeper keel than most steamboats. The outcome of this was that the first time Capt'n Bill tried to steam up to the wharf at Sacramento City the deep keel buried itself in the mud at the river bottom and stayed there, holding the *Goodman Castle* in midstream.

The folks of Sacramento City thought Wild Bill was crazy when he swam ashore and said he was ready to load. "Get her off that mud first," they said. "You're only making her heavier if you load your cargo." But Bill didn't even bother to hire a rowboat. He had a few thousand feet of lumber-logs to deliver upriver and so he made a raft of it and put his passengers aboard. Pushing it ahead of him, he swam back to the steamboat. After the passengers had walked up the stage of the *Goodman Castle* to safety aboard her, Bill just tore that raft apart and threw the logs into a neat pile on the deck.

Then Bill swam back to the shore, grabbed George Whipple's pure-bred white bull by the tail, dragged him into the water and, swimming to his boat, threw him aboard as easy as David let go the stone at Goliath. He miscalculated that throw some though, for the bull landed on the uppermost or the Texas deck of the boat and he was so irritated that he chased the passengers around until Bill came aboard and dragged him below where he belonged.

After his whole cargo was neatly stowed away, Bill made one last trip ashore. He went to the plow-works and bought the biggest plow in Sacramento City, and he went to the harness shop and bought a strong harness. When he came back to the river bank he hitched himself to the plow and walked right into the water dragging it behind him. A crowd stood on the banks and watched the swirling water above his head as Bill plowed down the mud-bank that was holding his boat. Nobody ever knew how many furrows he plowed before the *Goodman Castle* suddenly floated free and Bill came aboard dragging his plow behind him.

No sooner had he freshened up a bit after his hard job of underwater plowing than he had a look around to make sure that his passengers were comfortable. He was mighty annoyed when he came upon the most widely known of all the California river-boat gamblers, Mr. John Phillip Courtney, just about to cheat an innocent passenger out of his money in a game of cards. Indeed,

Bill was so annoyed that he picked up Mr. Courtney by the nape
of the neck and the seat of his checkered trousers and hurled him
toward the bank. Some people think he meant to throw him ashore
without wetting his magnificent apparel and that he miscalculated.
Others think he meant to make his throw a little short. Whoever
may be right the fact remains that Mr. Courtney landed kerflop
in the Sacramento River only a few yards from dry land.

This misadventure made the passengers on the *Goodman Castle*
so merry that they soon burst into a song, the song that all gold-
hunters of the California goldrush used to delight in. Try to imagine
you are a passenger on Captain Bill Corlett's steamboat and on
your way to find a gold mine for yourself as you sing it.

THE BANKS OF THE SACRAMENTO

In a brisk walking speed

Ho, boys, — ho! for Cal - - for - nia, O! There's plen - ty of gold, so I've been told, On the banks of the Sac - ra - men - to.

THE BANKS
OF THE SACRAMENTO

Ho, boys, ho! for California, O!
There's plenty of gold, so I've been told,
On the banks of the Sacramento.

Ho, boys, ho! for Calfornia, O!
As many folks say, it's far away
To the banks of the Sacramento.

The Wild White Horse

The Wild White Horse

ONLY A FEW PEOPLE have been lucky enough to behold the wild white horse of the western plains. It has been about a hundred years since the Kiowa Indians first told white men of him. The warriors who had seen him were so sure that he was bigger and faster than any horse could be that they made up strange stories about him. They said he was not a real animal but a drift of white mist that seemed to have legs and a mane and a tail, and they called him the Ghost Horse of the Prairies. New Englanders who travelled west and became westerners—a great many of them did that—used to say that they could tell a better story than that about the big animal. They said everybody in New England knows that the brave Vermont soldier, Ethan Allen, used to say that after he died he would like to come back to earth in the form of a big white horse. "Mark our words," the westerners-who-came-from-New England would say, "that big white runner is really the spirit of Ethan Allen cased in horseflesh."

Whatever he is, there are two things about the wild white horse of the western plains that most people agree on. He can run faster than any other horse and he does not grow old. No cowboy has ever owned a mustang swift enough to overtake him or even to come close enough for his rider to throw a lasso over the arching neck. And though the wild white horse of the western plains has been seen again and again through the years since the Kiowas described him, he is said to be as strong and as swift as when his beauty first dazzled the eyes of the red men. Out where the great herds of cattle roam the grassy prairies of America, lonely cowboys are still amazed sometimes to see him standing on a distant bluff, and his whiteness is very clear against the deep blue of the western sky, and the years seem to have made no change in him.

Only one human being, a little girl named Gretchen, has ever been close enough to the wild white horse of the western plains to touch him. One day Gretchen's father and mother had piled her and her two little sisters and all the family belongings into a big covered wagon, hitched their team of horses to it, and started westward. When they came to the shores of the Guadelupe River, Gretchen had become very tired of being bumped along inside the white walls of the wagon and asked her father if she could ride the gentle mare that ambled beside the team, carrying bags of corn-meal on her back. Gretchen's mother was afraid she would fall off if she rode the mare but her father told her to climb out of the wagon. After she was on the ground he lifted her to the mare's back and tied each of her legs to the bags so that she could not fall. Then Gretchen rode on happily.

About noon that day the wagon sank so deep into the mud beside the river that the horses could not pull it out. Gretchen made the mare stop and wait while her father looked for stones and branches to put under the wheels to keep them from slipping. It was so warm waiting in the sun, and Gretchen was so weary, that in a few minutes she was sound asleep.

The next thing she knew she was jouncing along very rapidly and the meal bags were flopping about her legs. She felt the wind against her face and opened her eyes in astonishment. The mare was galloping at a fearful speed trying to keep up with a tremendous white horse that loped easily ahead of her and looked back once in a while as if to make sure that she was following. Gretchen had never traveled so fast and she was so excited that she forgot to be frightened.

Before long the white horse led the way into a crooked, green valley between brown hills. A herd of horses waited at the end of it and when they saw the newcomers they rushed to greet them. Some of them smelled the bags to which Gretchen's legs were tied and began nipping at them. Their teeth came so close to Gretchen that she was frightened and began to cry.

Suddenly the white horse drove the others away and snapped the ropes that bound Gretchen's legs to the bags with his strong teeth. Holding her dress firmly between his strong jaws, he lifted Gretchen from the mare's back and set her down gently upon the ground at the side of a little water hole. After that he lifted the meal bags from the mare's back and dropped them in her lap.

Gretchen opened the bags and poured out a little pile of meal for each horse to eat. Then she helped herself, eating of the meal and making cups of her little hands to bring the water to her mouth. She was having a lot of fun at the white horse's cornmeal party. The horses ate and ate—and so did Gretchen. By the time everyone had had enough, evening had come and little stars were shining above the hills. The horses went away, then, all but the mare and the wild white horse. They stood near Gretchen all night long while she slept contentedly beside the water hole.

And when the sun's rays first shone down into the valley, the big white horse lifted Gretchen by her dress again and put her on the mare's broad back. After that he set out ahead of them and the mare followed. Soon Gretchen could see her father's covered wagon gleaming in the sun. The wild white horse of the western plains stopped and waited until the mare had taken Gretchen safely back to her father's arms. Then he loped off—moving easily as a morning cloud before the wind. As he disappeared in the distance Gretchen could hear the riders up ahead singing a song with a galloping rhythm. Whenever she heard it again it reminded her of the big white horse and it seemed to her his flying hooves carried the beat.

Let them beat it out for you now.

GOOD-BY OLD PAINT

Slow and swaying

My foot's in the stir - rup, my po - ny won't stan', I'm a- leav - in' Chey - enne, and I'm off for Mon - tan'.

I'm ridin' old Paint, I'm a-leading old Fan,
Good-by, little lady, I'm a-leavin' Cheyenne
Good-by, old Paint, I'm a-leavin' Cheyenne
Good-by, old Paint, I'm a-leavin' Cheyenne.

Old Paint's a good pony, he paces when he can,
Good morning, young lady, my horses won't stan'
Good-by, old Paint, I'm a-leavin' Cheyenne
Good-by, old Paint, I'm a-leavin' Cheyenne.

Pecos Bill

Pecos Bill

PECOS BILL DID NOT KNOW that he was not a coyote until he was
eighteen. When he was a baby his father and mother decided to
take Bill and his seventeen brothers and sisters west across the
great plains in a covered wagon. One day the wagon jounced
through an old dried-up water-hole and baby Bill bounced out.

The unsuspecting parents did not get around to counting the
children until supper time. When they discovered the baby was
gone, they were greatly distressed. They rode back along the
trail, looking frantically for him, but Bill was gone. A childless
couple of coyotes had adopted him and were already bringing
him up as all good little coyotes are brought up.

So Bill learned to sit on a hill and howl at the moon as mourn-
fully as his step-father, who was the most mournful howler of the
whole region.

When Bill was eighteen he was out howling one night when
he met a cowboy who praised his mournful notes highly but said:
"Wa-a-l, if you be a coyote, where's your tail?"

It was not until then that Bill realized that, as a coyote, he had short-comings, and made up his mind to become a cowboy. His eighteen years of experience at howling were a great help to him and it was not long before he was looked upon as the greatest cowboy in the world.

One day Bill was riding beside the Witchita River when he saw a cow-girl riding a catfish downstream. This strange steed was spread-eagling and sun-fishing and acting in general like a wild cayuse, but the girl rode him as quietly as if he had been a flat-bottomed skiff, and she was using only a surcingle for harness.

Bill was so delighted with her beauty and with the way she rode a fish that when she dismounted just outside the River-view Cafe he went right up to her and asked her to marry him. She was somewhat surprised at this but after looking Bill over for a minute or two she said that she would be agreeable to his idea if he would grant her two wishes. By this time Bill was so pleased with her that, like many another young cowboy in a similar fix, he said yes before he knew what was expected of him.

So the girl told him that her name was Sue and that her first request was for something to wear at the wedding—a bustle. Now a bustle looked something like a long narrow bird-cage with a string at each end. The string tied over the stomach in front, and the bird-cage part in the back, when properly covered, gave an impression of dependability to the wearer.

Bill looked all over the United States of America for a bustle suitable for his bride. Finally he found one made of whale-bone and steel and gave it to Sue, who was so pleased with it that she said she would marry him then and there if he would grant her second wish as soon as they were man and wife. Bill agreed and they were married. Then Sue said her second wish was to ride Bill's mustang that went by the rather annoying name of Widow-Maker.

Bill did not want to let her ride Widow-Maker, but he had promised and so he took the mustang aside and tried to explain how things were. He thought Widow-Maker understood and perhaps he did at the time, but when Sue got on his back and her skirts tickled his ribs the mustang forgot what he had been told and began to buck. Sue stuck on for a moment or two but one final pitch shook her loose and she fell off and landed on her new bustle—and bounced.

The first bounce, so cowboys say, took her over the lower horn of the new moon. She came back down, landed on the Rocky Mountains—and went right back up again. For three days Bill sat beside the Rocky Mountains watching her go up and down, begging her not to be so nervous. Finally he realized that she would eventually starve to death since the bouncing gave no signs of letting up—so he had to shoot her.

That broke Bill's heart and he sat there by the Rocky Mountains and began to cry. All that happened years ago but people who live out in Oklahoma and Texas say that on clear nights they can still see Sue bouncing if they watch carefully as she passes the round yellow moon. And as for Pecos Bill, he is still crying, they know, for it is his tears that make the famous border river that all Americans know as the Rio Grande.

Widow-Maker has a new master now. He is a lean and lanky cowboy who sings the night through to the galloping rhythms of Widow-Maker's hoofs.

Let's lope along beside him for a while and join in on "Git Along Cayuse, Git Along."

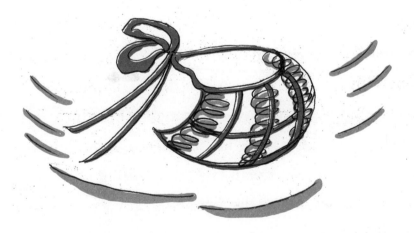

GET ALONG CAYUSE, GET ALONG

In a moderately loping pace

We're leav - ing here, and we're go - ing there, Get a - long cay - use, get a - long. We're long. There aint no wa - ter and there aint no shade, There

aint no   beer and   no   lem-on-ade;   But I

reck-on some-how we'll   make that   grade,   Get a

long cay - use,   get a - long;   get a -

long cay - use,   get a -   long.

Big-Foot Wallace

Big-Foot Wallace

IF YOU WERE BORN in one of the Eastern states of the South you have probably learned that the answer to the question: "What was the bravest and finest body of men ever organized under one command?" must always be, "As sure as shooting, the Army of Northern Virginia, sir." But if you first saw sunshine on the broad plains of the Southwest you are bound to give a very different answer: "By the great horn spoon—the Texas Rangers, sir."

Natives of other sections are satisfied to let their southern friends argue over which answer is correct. When you think of the Army of Northern Virginia you are likely to think of those brave leaders—Stonewall Jackson and Jeb Stuart and John Morgan—who fought so valiantly for the cause of the Confederacy. But if you think of the Texas Rangers you will be sure to remember Sam Houston and Mustang Gray and Big-Foot Wallace. If it had not been for the Rangers, Texas might not have won her independence and become a free country with an army and a navy; and if Texas had not become a free country, it might never have decided to become a part of the United States when it was invited.

Big-Foot was one of the bravest of all the Rangers who fought the Mexicans for the independence of Texas and the Indians for the protection of themselves and their neighbors. When it came to fighting, Big-Foot had as much sand in his craw—to use his own expression for gumption or courage—as the next man.

Big-Foot liked to tell about his adventures, and some of his stories are worth repeating. They have been changed some because the Texas Rangers of today realize that Big-Foot used his imagination in telling them and so they use *their* imaginations, too, and a story told under such circumstances usually gets to be quite a story.

One of the most amusing tales Big-Foot used to tell was about a tenderfoot writer who came to Texas to look up some things to put in a book which he expected to call "The Wayworn Wanderer of the Western Wilds." He brought his umbrella with him, all the way from the eastern states, and the Texas Rangers made great fun of him because he was never without it even when he rode with them. One day he strayed too far away from the troop and when he tried to return a band of hostile Indians attacked him. The Rangers could see what was happening but they realized that they were too far away to be able to help him. The plucky little man wheeled his horse and lit out for the main body of the Rangers with the Indians right after him yelling and shooting. Soon he knew his chances were slim, for the horses behind him were faster than his own. Just as they were upon him he had an idea. Loosing the furled umbrella strapped to his saddle he turned about and opened it full in the face of the leading pursuer. The sudden ballooning of the black surface threw both the Indian rider and his mount into a panic. The horse galloped off, completely out of control, and all the other Indian horses ran away, too. After that the Texas Rangers made no more fun of the little writer.

Big-Foot used to say that the Indians were not the only great danger to the Rangers, the monsters of the sandy waste were even more deadly. There was, he said, a spider in Texas as big as a peck measure, whose bite was so poisonous it could be cured only by listening to music. At the end of a hard day's work chasing Indians and horse-thieves and outlaws the Rangers always used to ride full-teakettle for their barracks where a big brass band would be playing to cure them of spider-bites they had just acquired. Their tarantula-boots made of alligator skin and centipede-hunting shirts of tanned rattlesnake hides were never enough protection from the spiders.

One of these spiders was deadlier than all the rest. It was called the Santafy (after the old town of Santa Fe) and even the best brass band in the country could not cure its victim. It had a hundred legs and a sting in every leg, and a forked tail with a sting in each fork, and a mouth equipped with fangs bigger than a rattlesnake's. If it stung a man with one leg he might live about an hour, but if it hit him with all legs he would be deader than a doornail in fifteen minutes. If it got a bite in as well, its victim would turn blue, then yellow, then bottle green, and kick the bucket in five minutes.

One day Big-Foot had wandered so far west he found himself in the purple Telechapi Mountains of California, where the winds blow so stiff that a man has to lean over until he is nearly horizontal to be able to stand. Sitting down to rest himself beside the road and to observe the gnarled oak trees, from which all bark had been blown, he felt a stinging sensation and saw that a Santafy had clamped itself upon his knee just above the top of his alligator-skin boot. All its legs and its mouth were already at work.

"Five minutes is all I've got," said Big-Foot to himself. "He's taken my sign in and I'll be deader than dead in just three hundred seconds, so I might as well just sit here and rest my face and hands."

He slapped the life out of the Santafy and sat counting the seconds. When he'd got to the end of the first fifty he heard a sharp pop and a long low sound like that of a clarinet. The wind had freshened and blown a knothole right out of one of those oaks. The air rushing through the hole was making the musical note. In another few seconds there was another pop, then another, then a whole series of them that sounded like the rattle of musketry. And after each one came the sound of a different note as the wind blew through the round hole where the knothole had been. Gradually the notes arranged themselves into a tune.

"I guess this is the jumping-off-place," said Big-Foot, and wondered if he would be looking comfortable when the next traveler out that way found him dead.

But the tune had begun to reach his ears. It got louder and louder and his leg began to feel better. In another minute he had begun to sing it. The music-cure was working. By the time the five minutes were up Big-Foot was feeling as full of dander as he ever had in his life, and he was bellowing out the Texas Rangers song so loud that the purple mountains sang it back to him.

See what you can do about setting up an echo with it.

TEXAS RANGERS

Very lively

About the age of six-teen,   I
I saw the In-dians com-ing.   I

joined a jol-ly band,   And
heard them give a yell,   My

marched thru West-ern Tex-as   Un-
feel-ings at that mo-ment   No

to the Ri-o Grande.   Our
hu-man tongue can tell.   We

cap - tain he in - formed us, Per -
fought them full nine hours, ——— And

haps he thought it right; ——— 'Be -
then the strife was done, Those

fore we reach the sta - tion,— Brave
In — di — ans were beat — en Be -

boys we'll have to 'fight.'
fore the set of sun.

Paul Bunyan

Paul Bunyan

Big Paul, Paul Bunyan of the north woods, is the greatest lumber-jack in the world. Whenever a big job of lumbering needs to be done, Paul is the one to call on to get it out of the way. If he likes the idea he will soon be coming, striding across the tops of the north-woods mountains, his blue ox, Babe, walking by his side and looking for all the world like an ox-shaped piece of the blue sky. Babe, as any lumberjack can tell you, has wide-spreading horns and the distance from the tip of one horn to the tip of the other is twenty-eight ax handles and a plug of Star Chewing tobacco.

Between them, Paul and Babe have never seen a job of lumber-ing they could not do without help. Once in a while they have needed a little luck on their side but it has always been around when they needed it. There was the time, for instance, when Paul and his crew got very tired of cutting down pines day after day. The woods did not seem to get any smaller, no matter how many trees their axes had laid low by suppertime, and Christmas was coming when all the lumberjacks in the camp wanted to be at home with their children. To make matters worse rain set in and every-body in camp began to worry for fear it would melt the river ice under the logs that had been cut and send the whole pile dashing

[238]

against the little dam they had built in the fall to hold back enough water to float their logs downstream to the sawmill. If the dam were to break all the water would go and there would be none to float the rest of the winter's cutting to the mill.

Paul got up early one morning and slung his double-blade ax over his shoulder. While his crew was at breakfast they could hear his ringing strokes deep in the woods. But when they came out to join him there were no woods, for Paul had been hard at work. He was just finishing off a little grove and the men stood around and admired the way he did it. As he swung the ax downward it would bite deep into the wood of a tree. Then he would raise the ax, swinging it far back, and the blade on the reverse side would bite into a tree behind him. In less time than it takes to tell about it both trees would be lying on the ground and Paul would be cutting down two more. Even as the crew stood and stared the last pair went down.

"Load them on the sledge, men," said Paul, "while I hitch up Babe."

Soon the whole winter's cutting was neatly piled on the sledge and Paul had hitched big blue Babe to the load.

"Get up!" said Paul.

Babe moved off easily enough, but to everyone's surprise the load did not budge. The harness with which Paul had hitched up Babe was of rawhide and the rain of the day before had soaked it thoroughly. Wet rawhide, as every woodsman knows, will some-

times outstretch rubber. Before anybody so much as got a chance
to talk about it Babe had reached the ice on the river, the rawhide
was still stretching and the load had not moved. Paul hurried down
to the bank of the river.

"Whoa!" he shouted.

Babe stopped beside a great rock that reared its head above
the surface of the ice. Swiftly Paul unhitched Babe and, holding
the harness tightly, he wound it around the rock three times.

"All we have to do now is sit around and wait," he said.

So Paul and Babe and all the crew sat down and waited.

About ten o'clock a wind sprang up and blew away the clouds.
The sun came out strong and both the wind and the sun began to
dry the rawhide harness. Soon, with a great creaking and groaning
the load began to move down toward the river. Dryer and dryer
became the rawhide, shrinking more and more. And with every
minute of shrinking it dragged the load a few feet farther.

Then from the river came a sound that worried everybody. It
was the first crack of the ice, melted and loosened up by the rains
of the week before and now by the warm sunlight. If it should break
up it would crush the dam and float off down stream carrying with
it the logs already piled there. Then there would be no more water
to carry the logs of the load that was now moving slowly toward
the river.

Paul and his lumberjacks lined up to watch the load go by and
cheered mightily as the groaning rawhide shrank another fifteen

yards. There was now a chance that the load would be on the ice before it broke up. More cracking noises came to the ears of the excited audience. Suddenly the ice began to break and float and pile up. In another minute its weight would break down the dam and the water would begin to go out. As if it understood what was happening the rawhide began to shrink faster and faster. The sun burned down fiercely and the load was fairly racing along. Just as the dam broke the sledge reached the edge of the river and plunged in. With a whoop every lumberjack on the bank leaped on a log and rode it as the water rushed it downstream. The winter's work was done. Now they could collect a whole season's pay and be home for Christmas as well.

An hour later all the lumberjacks were at the bunkhouse, saying good-by and Merry Christmas to Paul and Babe. And before setting out for home they sang in roaring chorus a song they had made up about themselves. It is called "The Shantyman's Life."

Sing it as if you were one of the jolly lumberjacks looking forward to Christmas at home.

THE SHANTYMAN'S LIFE

Wearily

Oh, a shant-y man's life is a wear-i-some life, Al-though some think we have no care. Ly-ing in the shant-y_ so bleak and so chill, While the cold and storm-y win-try winds do

Oh, we swing the bright ax from cold morn — ing 'til night, In the midst of the for — est drear

blow; And as soon as the day-light does ap-

pear, To the wild snowy woods we go.

But when spring does set in,
Double hardships begin,
When the waters are piercing cold;
We are dripping and wet and our fingers benumbed,
And our pike poles we scarce can hold.
Then the rocks and sands
Give hard work to all hands,
On the sturdy banded raft we have to steer;
And the rapids we run,
They seem to us fun,
For we're void of all slavish fear.

PUBLISHER'S NOTE

The text of this book is set in Caledonia, a Linotype face designed by W. A. Dwiggins, the man responsible for so much that is good in contemporary book design and typography. Caledonia belongs to the family of printing types called "modern face" by printers—a term used to mark the change in style of type-letters that occurred about 1800. It has all the hard-working feet-on-the-ground qualities of the Scotch Modern face plus the liveliness and grace that is integral in every Dwiggins "product" whether it be a simple catalogue cover or an almost human puppet.

The book was printed in offset lithography by WILLIAM C. D. GLASER of Long Island City, New York, and bound by H. WOLFF of New York.